The Heinemann Science Scheme

Book 1

Ian Bradley • Peter Gale • Mark Winterbottom

This book is dedicated to the following people:
From Ian Bradley: To Harry Smith (1925–1999) who never stopped learning.
From Peter Gale: To Pam, Nicola and Charlotte, for all your help and support.
From Mark Winterbottom: To Sal, for putting up with never seeing me.

Heinemann Educational Publishers
Halley Court, Jordan Hill, Oxford, OX2 8EJ
Part of Harcourt Education
Heinemann is the registered trademark
of Harcourt Education Ltd

© Ian Bradley, Peter Gale, Mark Winterbottom 2001

First published 2001

ISBN 0 435 582 429

06 05 04
10 9 8 7 6 5

Edited by Mary Korndorffer and Helen Juden

Designed and typeset by Cambridge Publishing Management

Illustrated by Hardlines

Cover photo by Stone.

Picture research by Thelma Gilbert

Printed and bound in Great Britain by The Bath Press Ltd, Bath

Acknowledgements
The authors and publishers would like to thank
Michael O'Mara Books Ltd for permission to use the extract
from 'Lost in the Moors' by Diana Pullein Thompson from
'Best Horse Stories' 1991; HMSO for the Highway Code data
on p129.

The publishers have made every effort to trace the copyright
holders, but if they have inadvertently overlooked any, they
will be pleased to make the necessary arrangements at the
first opportunity.

The authors and publishers would like to thank the following for
permission to use photographs:

p3 T: SPL B: SPL/Michael Abbey. p5 & 6: BiophotoAssociates.
p8 TL: SPL/Andrew Leonard TR: SPL/BSIP VEM BL: SPL/John
Walsh M & BR: Biophoto Associates. p10: SPL/Astrid & Hans
Frieder Michler. p12 L: Oxford Scientific Films R: Harry Smith.
p14: Oxford Scientific Films. p15 (1) and (2): Roger Scruton (3):
Oxford Scientific Films (4): Bruce Coleman. p22: Bubbles.
p25: SPL/Peter Ryan. p28 TL: OSF ML: OSF MR: Natural Visions B:
OSF. p29 T: Roger Scruton M & B: OSF. p31 T: OSF B: Andrew
Lambert. p32 L T & B: Natural Visions ML T & B: OSF MR T & B:
Natural Visions R T: Natural Visions R B: OSF. p33 T (2): OSF M (2):
Roger Scruton B R (2): OSF B L: Still Pictures. p34: OSF.
p35 T L (1) & (2): Bruce Coleman T M: Still Pictures T R (1) & (2):
OSF B: OSF. p 38: OSF. p39 T L: Game Conservancy Trust/John
Darling M R: Bruce Coleman M L: OSF T R: Bruce Coleman M M:
Roger Scruton T M L: Bruce Coleman T M R: OSF B L: OSF B R:
Natural Visions. p40 T & M L: OSF M R: Bruce Coleman B L:
Natural Visions B R: OSF. p43 T: Holt Studios M & B: OSF.
p46 T: SPL M & B: OSF. p48, 52 & 53: Roger Scruton.
p54 – 57: Andrew Lambert. p58 T: Roger Scruton B L: SPL/Dr
Jeremey Burgess B R: SPL/Adam Hart Davis. p59: Environmental
Images. p60: Roger Scruton. p62 T L: Oxford Scientific Films T R &
B R: Roger Scruton B L: Still Pictures. p63: Andrew Lambert.
p64 T: Roger Scruton M & B: Andrew Lambert. p65: Andrew
Lambert. p67 T L: Roger Scruton T M L: Geoscience Features T M R
& T R: Roger Scruton B: Andrew Lambert. p68 T: Roger Scruton B:
Environmental Images. p69: Andrew Lambert. p70 L 1 & 2: Roger
Scruton R 1 & 2: Robert Harding M: Spectrum. p72: Andrew
Lambert. p74: Bridgeman Art Library/Vatican Museums & Galleries.
p75 T R: Roger Scruton B R: Andrew Lambert M L: Oxford Scientific
Films M R: Robert Harding B L: Bruce Coleman M M: Roger
Scruton. p76 & 77: Andrew Lambert. p78 & 79: Roger Scruton.
p80 T: Geoscience Features M: Andrew Lambert B: Oxford Scientific
Films. p82 & 83: Andrew Lambert. p84 T & B: Andrew Lambert M:
Bruce Coleman. p85: Andrew Lambert. p86 T: Geoscience Features
M T: Salt Union MB Oxford Scientific Films B Roger Scruton.
p87 & 88: Andrew Lambert. p89: SPL/Dr Jeremy Burgess.
p90 T L: Roger Scruton T R: Nigel Rumble M: Andrew Lambert B:
Oxford Scientific Films. p91 & 92: Andrew Lambert.
p93 Ian Bradley. p94 & 95: Andrew Lambert. p96 T: Colorsport M:
Environmental Images. p97 – 99: Andrew Lambert. p100 T: Roger
Scruton. M: Environmental Images. B: Oxford Scientific Films.
p103: Oxford Scientific Films. p104 M: Bubbles B: Andrew Lambert.
p108 & 109: Andrew Lambert. p110: Peter Gale. p113: Andrew
Lambert. p114: Roger Scruton. p119: SPL. p120 – 123: Andrew
Lambert. p124 T: Andrew Lambert M & B: Spectrum. p125: Andrew
Lambert. p126 T: Alan Edwards M: Roger Scruton B: Colorsport.
p127 T: Robert Harding. p130 & 131: Andrew Lambert. p144: SPL.
p32 T M L, p35T M & B M, p43 B L, p46 L M, p75 R M, p96 B,
p102 T M, p104 T, p106 – 107, p127 L M & B, p132, 137, 141, 143,
145 photodisc.

Welcome to Heinemann Science Scheme!

This is the first book in a series of three which covers all the science you need to learn at Key Stage 3.

It is divided into twelve units. Each unit has topics which take up a double page spread each. On each double page spread you will find:

● **A topic checklist at the start with this heading:**

TOPIC CHECKLIST

This tells you what you will study on that double page spread.

● **Questions as you go along like this:**

ⓑ What is the solute in salt solution?

These are quick questions which help you check that you understand the explanations before you carry on.

● **Questions in a box at the end of the spread with this heading:**

QUESTIONS

These help you draw together all the material on the spread.

Important words are highlighted in bold on the pages. They all appear in a glossary at the back of the book with their meanings so that you can look them up easily as you work through the book.

As you study Heinemann Science Scheme you will also be doing practical activities and extra questions and assignments from the teacher's pack which goes with it, as well as tests which help you and your teachers keep track of how you're doing.

We hope you enjoy studying science with Heinemann Science Scheme.

Contents

A Cells

WHAT ARE LIVING THINGS MADE FROM?

> **TOPIC CHECKLIST**
>
> ● What are the characteristics of life?
> ● What are organs?
> ● What are organs made of?

What are the characteristics of life?

All living things (**organisms**) have some features in common. They all need food for energy. Plants make their own food. Animals get it by eating plants or other animals. The process of making and using food is called **nutrition**.

All living things **move**. It is obvious how animals move because they move their whole bodies from place to place. But plants can also move. For example, they can turn towards the light.

Living things also need to **grow**. They all start off small and then grow taller, longer, fatter or thicker. They also **reproduce**. That means they make new living things like themselves. For example, humans and other animals make babies. The general name for the young of all living things is offspring.

What are organs?

There are lots of different **organs** in your body. These organs work together so that our body can carry out the processes of life. Each organ has a different job. The diagram opposite shows some of the organs in our body.

ⓐ Which organs in the body process our food?

ⓑ Which organs help us move?

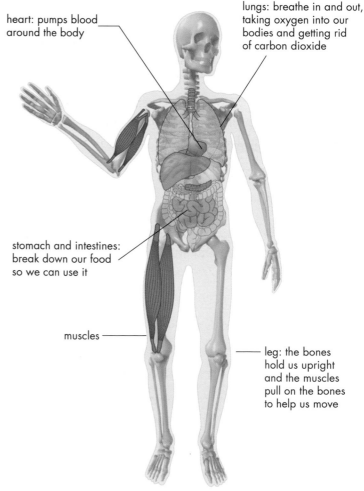

heart: pumps blood around the body

lungs: breathe in and out, taking oxygen into our bodies and getting rid of carbon dioxide

stomach and intestines: break down our food so we can use it

muscles

leg: the bones hold us upright and the muscles pull on the bones to help us move

Plants also have organs which are involved in life's processes. Look at the diagram to see what they do.

c **Where does the plant make its food?**

d **Which part of a plant is important in making new plants?**

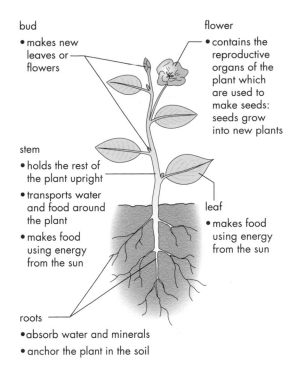

bud
• makes new leaves or flowers

flower
• contains the reproductive organs of the plant which are used to make seeds: seeds grow into new plants

stem
• holds the rest of the plant upright
• transports water and food around the plant
• makes food using energy from the sun

leaf
• makes food using energy from the sun

roots
• absorb water and minerals
• anchor the plant in the soil

What are organs made of?

Every animal and plant, and all of their organs, are made of tiny building blocks called **cells**. Cells are so small they can only be seen under the microscope.

Cells are too small to do much by themselves and so they work together in groups called **tissues**. A tissue contains lots of similar cells which do the same job. Organs are made of several different tissues. You will learn more about tissues and organs in Topic A5.

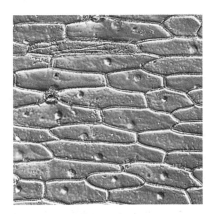

Onion skin cells

QUESTIONS

1 Make a list of the characteristics shared by all living things.

2 Complete the sentences:

   a) A group of cells which do the same job is called a _____.

   b) _____ are made up of a number of tissues.

3 What is the job of the heart in a human being?

4 What is the job of your lungs?

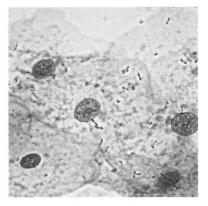

Human cheek cells

USING THE MICROSCOPE

TOPIC CHECKLIST

- What are microscopes used for?
- What is magnification?
- How do you look at something using a microscope?
- How do you draw something seen with a microscope?

What are microscopes used for?

Microscopes are used for looking at very small things like cells. Although there are lots of different types of microscope, they all have similar parts which enable them to do the same job. Look at the picture of the microscope opposite to find out what each part does.

What is magnification?

When a microscope makes an object look bigger, we say the object has been magnified. **Magnification** is how much bigger the object *looks* than it actually is.

- On each microscope, there are two **lenses** which magnify the object: the objective lens and the eyepiece lens.

- You can find out how much each magnifies by looking on the side of the lens. For instance, the eyepiece lens is normally ×10 (*times ten*) magnification. That means it makes an object look ten times bigger than it actually is.

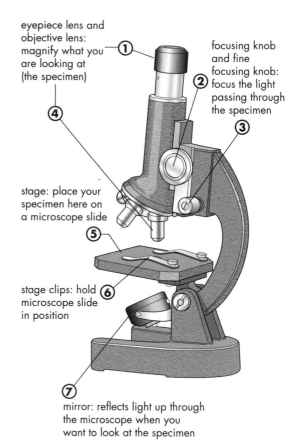

eyepiece lens and objective lens: magnify what you are looking at (the specimen) — ①

focusing knob and fine focusing knob: focus the light passing through the specimen — ②

③

④

stage: place your specimen here on a microscope slide

⑤

stage clips: hold ⑥ microscope slide in position

⑦

mirror: reflects light up through the microscope when you want to look at the specimen

You can work out the total magnification produced by both lenses together:

Total magnification = magnification of objective lens × magnification of eyepiece lens

For example, the picture of onion cells on page 3 was taken using an objective lens of ×10 magnification and an eyepiece lens of ×10 magnification.

ⓐ **What was the total magnification?**

How do you look at something using a microscope?

1. To look at an object under the microscope, it must be thin enough for light to pass through it. Take a thin slice, or peel a thin layer from what you want to look at.

2. Place this (the **specimen**) on a microscope **slide** (a rectangular piece of glass).

3. You may need to add a drop of coloured dye (a **stain**) to make it easier to see. Otherwise, just put a drop of water on the specimen to stop it drying out.

4. To stop the liquid getting onto the objective lens, cover the specimen (and the drop of stain or water) with a thin piece of glass called a **cover slip**.

5. Lower the cover slip onto the specimen as shown in the diagram. It stops air bubbles forming.

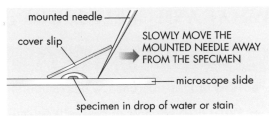

Lowering a cover slip onto a specimen

6. To look at the specimen, put the slide on the microscope's stage. The specimen itself must be in the middle of the stage (under the objective lens) to be able to see it.

7. **Focus** the microscope to see the specimen clearly.

(b) **Why is it important to avoid air bubbles?**

How do you draw something seen with a microscope?

The drawing of the photograph opposite shows you how to do a really good drawing of what you can see using the microscope. Use the following tips to help.

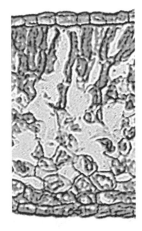

- Use a sharp pencil.
- Don't colour or shade any parts of your drawing.
- Make sure your drawing occupies at least half a page.
- Don't draw your specimen inside a circle.
- Give your drawing a heading.
- Calculate the total magnification and write it on your drawing.
- If you have time, try to estimate the size of your specimen by looking at a ruler under the microscope and measuring the width of the field of view you can see. Then compare this with how far across the field of view your specimen stretches.

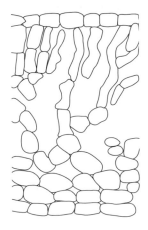

QUESTIONS

1 What is a microscope used for?

2 a) Which is nearest the eye: the eyepiece lens, or the objective lens?

   b) What do you put on the microscope stage?

3 a) What does the word *magnification* mean?

   b) You are looking at some cells using a microscope. Your eyepiece lens has a magnification of ×10. Your objective lens has a magnification of ×25. What is the total magnification?

4 Why do you think you should avoid shading or colouring parts of your diagram?

WHAT ARE CELLS LIKE?

TOPIC CHECKLIST

- How did the microscope help scientists to discover cells?
- What do plant and animal cells look like?
- What do the parts of the cell do?

How did the microscope help scientists to discover cells?

Before 1665, most biologists thought that living things were made of 'primitive blastema'. They did not really understand what this was, but still thought that every living organism was made of it.

It was only when Robert Hooke, an English scientist, designed the first microscope in 1665, that the theory began to change. He used it to look at a thin slice of cork (which comes from the bark of trees).

Inside the cork, he saw lots of tiny boxes which he called cells. This means 'little room' in Latin (a language which many scientists used in those days). Cells had been invisible to people before the invention of his microscope.

As more and more scientists began to use microscopes, cells were discovered in more and more living things. In 1838 some scientists proposed a cell theory. They had looked at a large number of plants and animals and found cells in all of them. They decided (correctly) that *all* animals and plants were made of cells.

After this, scientists started to work hard on improving their microscopes and used them to look at every sort of living thing. We now have much more powerful microscopes, which show us much more detail. The pictures show cells seen under microscopes of different power.

(a) Why were cells only discovered in 1665?

(b) Why did scientists in the nineteenth century decide that all animals and plants were made of cells?

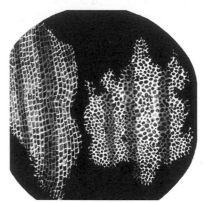

What Robert Hooke saw under his microscope

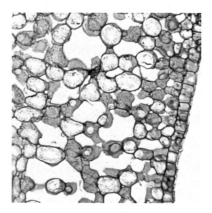

Plant cells seen under low power

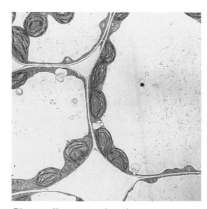

Plant cells seen using the most powerful microscope

What do plant and animal cells look like?

As microscopes got better and better, other biologists realised that plant and animal cells looked slightly different. They share some of the same features, but plant cells also have some extra features which animal cells do not have.

Microscopes always give you a flat picture of a cell. But cells are not flat: animal cells are like tiny bags, and plant cells are like tiny boxes. You see a flat picture looking down the microscope because you see a slice across the cell.

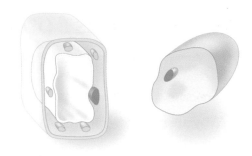

Plant cell   *Animal cell*

What do the parts of the cell do?

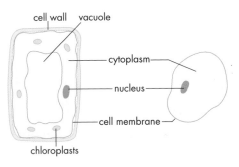

Plant cell   *Animal cell*

The **nucleus**, **cytoplasm** and **cell membrane** have the same jobs in plant and animal cells.

- The **nucleus** controls what happens inside the cell.
- The **cytoplasm** occupies most of the cell. The cell's chemical reactions happen here.
- The **cell membrane** holds the cytoplasm together and controls what goes in and out of the cell.

Those features found only in plant cells have different jobs.

- The **cell wall** is strong and stops the cell changing shape, collapsing or bursting.
- The large **vacuole** contains the cell sap (a store of water, salt and sugar).
- The **chloroplasts** catch light energy and use it to make food.

c **Imagine you have been shrunk so you are much smaller than a cell. Describe your journey through a plant cell.**

d **Why can't animals make their own food?**

QUESTIONS

1 Which of these features would you find in an animal cell?

a) nucleus   d) large vacuole

b) chloroplasts   e) cell wall

c) cytoplasm   f) cell membrane

2 Write down the function of each of the following parts of the cell:

a) chloroplast   c) cell membrane

b) nucleus   d) vacuole

3 People's ideas about what living things are made of have changed since 1600. Make a timeline to explain how they have changed.

WHAT DO CELLS DO?

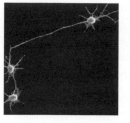
a

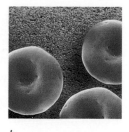
b

Are cells all the same?

Look at these pictures of cells. They look very different to the cells we have seen already. However, each one is either a plant or an animal cell. By looking at the cells' features, you can tell which is which. Remember: animal cells do not have a cell wall, chloroplasts or a large vacuole.

c

a Which pictures are animal cells and which are plant cells?

Why are cells different?

Some animals and plants are made of just one cell, or just a few cells. All of their cells have to carry out all of the processes of life. However, larger organisms are more complicated: they have different organs to do different jobs. The cells which make up these organs also have particular jobs. The shape and structure of each cell helps each one to do its job properly. We say the cells are **specialised** because they have special structures for special functions.

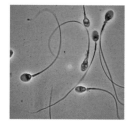
d

e

Red blood cell

The red colour of our blood comes from the millions of red blood cells which it contains. They carry oxygen from the air in the lungs to all the body cells. The body needs a lot of oxygen so the red blood cell has no nucleus. This gives it space to carry as much oxygen as possible.

Sperm cell

This is produced by a male animal and joins with the egg from a female animal to form the first cell of a new baby. It often has a long way to travel. If it is made by a fish, it has to swim through water to find the egg. If it is made by a land animal, it has to swim through parts of the female's body to find the egg. To help it swim such a long way, it has a long tail.

cell membrane
cytoplasm
nucleus

Egg cell

Egg cells are large so they can store a lot of food. Once the egg and sperm have joined together, the new baby needs the food to help it develop properly.

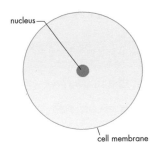

Nerve cell

Nerve cells carry messages around your body. For example, if you want to move your hand, your brain sends a message through a nerve cell to your hand telling it to move. Nerve cells are very long so they can carry messages a long way. They are also branched at the ends to pick up and deliver messages from and to lots of different places.

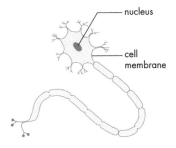

Epithelium cells

These cover and protect the surface of organs in animals. They are usually flat and fit together in sheets to cover the organs properly.

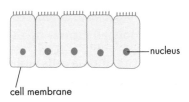

Root hair cell

You can see these on the roots of plants. Because they are very long and thin, they can take in a lot of water from the soil.

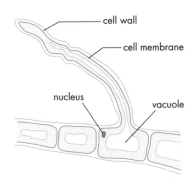

QUESTIONS

1 Which cells have the following jobs?

  a) absorb water from the soil

  b) carry oxygen around the human body

  c) transmit messages around the human body

2 How are these cells specialised for doing their jobs?

  a) sperm cell   c) epithelium cell

  b) egg cell   d) root hair cell

3 You need different cells to do different jobs. Why can't one type of cell do all those jobs?

TISSUES AND ORGANS

What is a tissue?

Cells which do the same job, and look the same, are usually found grouped together. These groups of cells are called tissues. Tissues are found in both plants and animals.

Muscle tissue is made up of millions of muscle cells. One muscle cell could not pull very much on its own. When lots of muscle cells are grouped together, they can pull on bones and make them move.

Xylem *(pronounced zylem)* tissue is found in plants. Xylem cells line up end to end to form long tubes, which transport water around the plant. One xylem cell on its own could not transport water very far. Lots of xylem cells together can transport water from the roots, all the way up the stem to the leaves.

ⓐ **Why can muscle cells and xylem cells only do their jobs when they group together?**

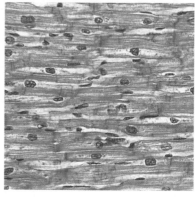

Muscle tissue

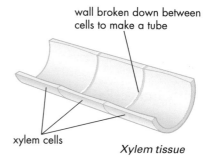

wall broken down between cells to make a tube

xylem cells

Xylem tissue

What is an organ?

A group of several different tissues is called an organ. Although each tissue does a different job in an organ, together they make sure the organ does *its* job. A house is rather like an organ. Its job is to give a warm, dry place in which to live. The walls and the roof are rather like tissues: they keep out the cold air and the rain. The bricks and the roof tiles are rather like cells: they make the walls and the roof.

ⓑ **Try to think of one other 'tissue' inside a house. What is its job? What are the cells called from which it is made?**

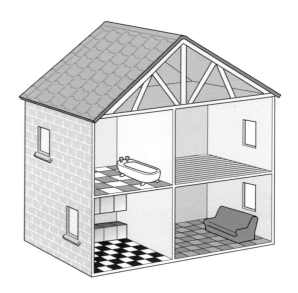

Both animals and plants have organs. Look at the rabbit's leg. The leg is an organ made of several different tissues. These tissucs help the leg to move.

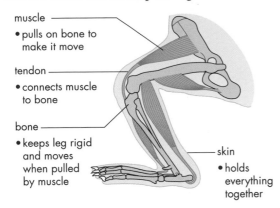

muscle
• pulls on bone to make it move

tendon
• connects muscle to bone

bone
• keeps leg rigid and moves when pulled by muscle

skin
• holds everything together

c **Name three tissues which are in your arm.**

Look at the diagram of the leaf. Its job is to make food. To do so, it needs to catch light from the sun.

The leaf has **palisade tissue** which makes most of the food, and **epidermal tissue** which holds it all together and protects it. Because the palisade tissue is near the top of the leaf, it can get as much light as possible. Organs work better if their tissues are in the best position to do their job.

d **Suggest why the epidermal cells are clear or transparent. Think about how easily light can pass through and why that may be important.**

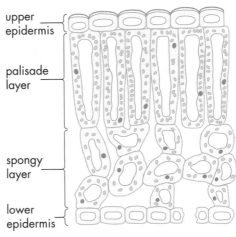

upper epidermis

palisade layer

spongy layer

lower epidermis

Inside a leaf

QUESTIONS

1 a) What are tissues made of?

b) What are organs made of?

2 Suggest one type of tissue which you may find in each of these organs:

    a) leaf   **c)** heart

    b) stem

3 What do these tissues do?

    a) nervous

    b) epithelial

    c) muscle

    d) palisade

HOW ARE NEW CELLS MADE?

How do living things grow?

Most living things start life very small, for example as a small seedling or a baby. But they grow, sometimes to huge sizes. Look at the picture of the young redwood tree in California. When fully grown, this will become one of the tallest trees in the world.

But how does it get so big? The answer is that its cells divide to make new cells, and each of these new cells grows larger.

How do cells divide?

All cells divide in the same way. Cell division starts with the nucleus. The nucleus contains the information which controls the cell. This information copies itself and the nucleus divides into two. The two nuclei (the plural of nucleus) produced each contain enough information to run their own cell. Because of this, the cell itself then divides into two as well.

A young redwood *A fully-grown giant redwood*

ⓐ Why is the information in the nucleus copied before it divides?

ⓑ Why does the nucleus divide first?

You can recognise cells which have just been made by **cell division**; they are only half the size of normal cells. They then grow until they are normal size.

Children grow a lot in childhood and adolescence. They grow so much because their cells are dividing quickly.

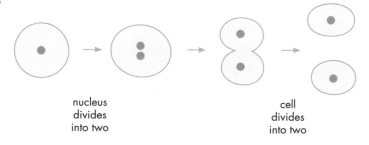

nucleus
divides
into two

cell
divides
into two

How are new organisms made?

Many living things make new organisms (reproduce) when special cells from the male and the female join together. In plants, the male cell is a pollen cell and the female cell is an egg cell.

To make a new plant, the pollen cell must join together with the egg cell. This is called **fertilisation**. The pollen cell and the egg cell only carry half as much information in their nuclei as ordinary cells. When they join, they make one new cell which has a full set of information: half comes from the pollen cell nucleus and half comes from the egg cell nucleus. This new cell then divides normally (and very quickly) to form a new plant.

Ⓒ **When a pollen cell and an egg cell join together, how many new cells do they form?**

How does fertilisation happen in plants?

Fertilisation happens inside flowers. Egg cells are found in the **ovary**. Pollen cells are found inside pollen grains, which are made by the anthers. Pollen grains are either blown by the wind, or carried by insects to other flowers. When the pollen grain arrives on the stigma of a new flower, we say that **pollination** has happened.

ⓓ **What is the difference between fertilisation and pollination?**

Before fertilisation can happen, the pollen cell has to get from the pollen grain to the egg inside the ovary.

- The pollen cell grows a tube out of the pollen grain and down through the stigma and the style into the ovary.

- The nucleus of the pollen cell moves down the tube and into the ovary.

- When the pollen cell nucleus and the egg cell nucleus join together, fertilisation happens.

- This makes the first cell of a new plant.

This new cell divides and divides, growing to form an embryo and a seed. The seed can then grow into a new plant.

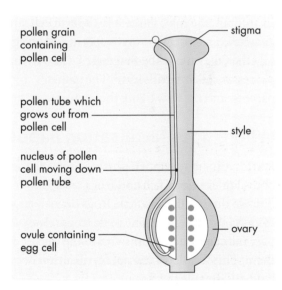

pollen grain containing pollen cell — stigma

pollen tube which grows out from pollen cell

nucleus of pollen cell moving down pollen tube

style

ovule containing egg cell

ovary

QUESTIONS

1 What two things do cells do when plants and animals grow?

2 Describe how a cell divides in two steps.

3 What are the names of the special cells which join to form a new plant?

4 Write a flow chart to show the path of the pollen cell nucleus from the anther where it is made, to the ovary where it fertilises the female egg cell.

B Reproduction

HOW DOES A NEW LIFE START?

TOPIC CHECKLIST

- What is fertilisation?
- Where does fertilisation happen?
- Why do animals care for their offspring in different ways?

What is fertilisation?

In Unit A, we saw that animals and plants produce special cells to reproduce. These are called **sex cells** or **gametes**. In animals, the male gamete is a **sperm cell**, and the female gamete is an **egg cell**. When a sperm and an egg join together, they make the first cell of a new living thing. This process is called fertilisation. The gametes come from the parents, and the new living thing created is the offspring.

Where does fertilisation happen?

Fertilisation may happen outside or inside the female's body. For example, fish and frogs release their gametes outside their bodies. Female frogs deposit large numbers of eggs into the water. The male frogs release their sperm over the eggs. The sperm swim to the eggs and fertilise them. This is called **external fertilisation** because it happens outside the female's body.

In land animals, the male animal puts his sperm inside the female's body. Once it is there, it swims to find the egg. This is called **internal fertilisation** because it happens inside the female's body.

ⓐ Draw and label diagrams of an egg cell and a sperm cell.

ⓑ Which parent produces the sperm cell and which the egg cell?

ⓒ Only animals which live in water can fertilise their eggs externally. Why do you think this is?

Why do animals care for their offspring in different ways?

Frogs

Once the eggs are fertilised, the male and female frog have nothing more to do with them. The young develop inside the fertilised eggs (frog spawn) and then hatch out into the water.

When they hatch, the offspring (tadpoles) must find food on their own, and look after themselves. Many eggs are eaten by other animals before they hatch out and many tadpoles do not survive to turn into frogs. To make sure at least *some* offspring survive, the parents have to release a lot of gametes.

Humans

Most land animals produce far fewer offspring at one time than fish and frogs. For example, women usually produce only one egg every month. A man releases his sperm inside the woman's body so that they are close to the egg and have a good chance of fertilising it. The developing baby is then protected inside its mother for nine months before it is born.

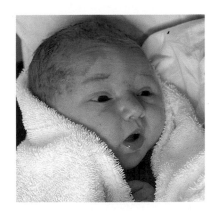

When a baby is born, it is completely unable to survive without adults. Until it grows up, the child is looked after by its parents. The change to adulthood usually takes about eighteen years.

d **Why do humans take so much care of their children compared to frogs?**

Other mammals

All mammals protect their offspring before birth by carrying them inside the mother for varying amounts of time. However, most mammals do not actually care for their offspring for very long.

Look at the picture of the foal, which is ready to walk within a few minutes of being born, and the puppies which only need looking after for about twelve weeks after birth. Because the puppies need looking after for only a short period of time, the parents have more energy to make more puppies. Dogs may give birth to up to ten puppies at once.

QUESTIONS

1 Write a sentence to describe fertilisation.

2 Why do fish and frogs make so many gametes?

3 Animals which have only one or two offspring at once take care of them for longer. Explain why.

4 Make a table showing the similarities and differences between reproduction in frogs and humans.

HOW DOES FERTILISATION HAPPEN?

What do the reproductive organs do?

In humans, fertilisation happens inside the woman's body (internal fertilisation). A man's **reproductive organs** make sperm and place them into the woman's reproductive organs.

A woman's reproductive organs make eggs, provide a place for fertilisation to happen, and provide a place for a new baby to grow and develop.

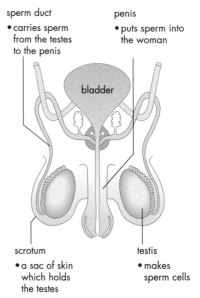

sperm duct
- carries sperm from the testes to the penis

penis
- puts sperm into the woman

bladder

scrotum
- a sac of skin which holds the testes

testis
- makes sperm cells

Male reproductive organs

What happens during sexual intercourse?

For fertilisation to happen, the man must place his sperm inside the woman. To do this, a man and a woman must have **sexual intercourse**.

During sexual intercourse, the man's **penis** becomes stiff and erect, and it is pushed into the woman's **vagina**. It can become stiff because it is made of soft, spongy tissue, which swells with blood when the man is sexually excited.

Once inside the woman's vagina, the sperm cells leave the penis and swim through the **cervix**, into the **uterus** and up into the **oviducts**.

a Where are sperm cells made and which tube do they travel through to leave the penis?

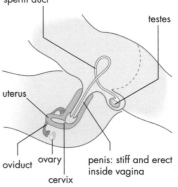

sperm cells travel from the testes out into the vagina through the sperm duct

testes

uterus

oviduct   ovary

cervix

penis: stiff and erect inside vagina

What happens during sexual intercourse?

When an egg is released from one of the woman's ovaries it moves down the oviduct where it meets the sperm. When one of the sperm joins together with one of the eggs, fertilisation has happened, and the first cell of a new human being is made.

ⓑ **Copy the diagram of a woman's reproductive organs. Draw an arrow to show the pathway of sperm after they leave the vagina. Mark with a cross the place where fertilisation happens.**

It is only possible for one sperm cell to fertilise an egg cell. Once a sperm has got inside the egg, the egg makes a protective coat to stop any more getting in.

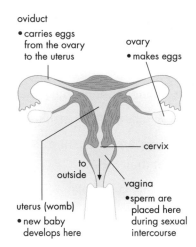

Female reproductive organs

oviduct
● carries eggs from the ovary to the uterus

ovary
● makes eggs

cervix

to outside

vagina
● sperm are placed here during sexual intercourse

uterus (womb)
● new baby develops here

Why are sperm cells and egg cells good at their job?

A sperm cell must swim to the egg cell, and penetrate the thick membrane of the egg cell to get inside. Look at the diagram to see the features which help sperm cells to do this successfully.

Egg cells do not need to swim anywhere. Because of this, their size does not matter and they can store a lot of food for the developing embryo.

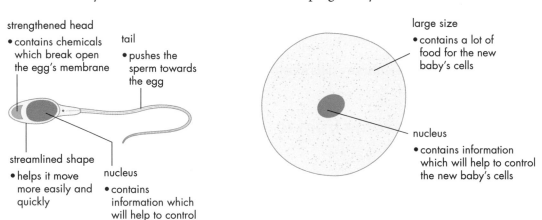

strengthened head
● contains chemicals which break open the egg's membrane

tail
● pushes the sperm towards the egg

streamlined shape
● helps it move more easily and quickly

nucleus
● contains information which will help to control the new baby's cells

Sperm cell

large size
● contains a lot of food for the new baby's cells

nucleus
● contains information which will help to control the new baby's cells

Egg cell

What is infertility?

Sometimes, fertilisation does not happen. This could be because the man or woman does not produce enough sperm or eggs. When a man does not produce enough sperm, we say he has a low sperm count. Women may have blocked oviducts, stopping sperm from swimming up to meet the egg.

QUESTIONS

1 Which organs make: a) sperm and b) eggs?

2 List three ways that sperm cells are adapted to fertilisation.

3 List three things which may stop a couple having children.

4 Why is it important that only one sperm cell fertilises each egg?

5 Find out three things about how doctors treat infertility.

WHAT HAPPENS AFTER FERTILISATION?

- What happens immediately after fertilisation?
- Where do the instructions come from to make a new human being?
- How are twins made?

What happens immediately after fertilisation?

When a sperm fertilises an egg, it makes a new cell (the **zygote**); the first cell of a new human being.

Immediately after fertilisation, the zygote divides into two. These two cells divide to make four cells, and these four cells divide to make eight cells. Cell division continues to happen over and over again as the ball of cells passes down the oviduct into the uterus. A ball of dividing cells is called an **embryo**. When it reaches the uterus, it burrows (**implants** itself) into the uterus wall, and the woman is **pregnant**.

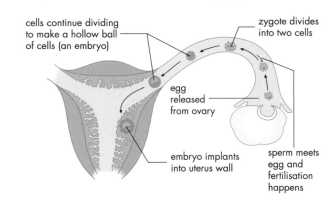

cells continue dividing to make a hollow ball of cells (an embryo)

zygote divides into two cells

egg released from ovary

embryo implants into uterus wall

sperm meets egg and fertilisation happens

ⓐ **How many times do you think the embryo's cells must divide before a new baby is made?**

Where do the instructions come from to make a new human being?

In each cell in your body, the nucleus contains a set of instructions. These instructions run the cell, and help to run your whole body. For example, the instructions inside your cells control what you look like.

Almost all your body cells have a nucleus which contains a full set of instructions (they wouldn't work very well otherwise!). But imagine if sperm and egg cells also had a full set of instructions. When they joined together in fertilisation, a zygote with a double set of instructions would be made.

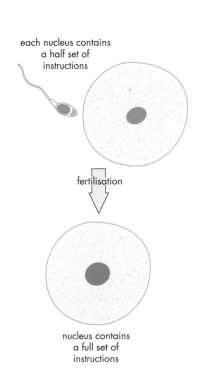

each nucleus contains a half set of instructions

fertilisation

nucleus contains a full set of instructions

ⓑ **What do you think a person would look like if they had a double set of instructions in each cell?**

In fact, any zygote with a double set of instructions soon dies. To stop zygotes like this being made, the nucleus of the sperm cell and egg cell only contain a half set of instructions. Therefore, after fertilisation, the zygote nucleus contains only one full set of instructions.

But when you make sperm or eggs in your testes or ovaries, which half of the instructions do you put into them? Well, imagine the instructions are like books and there are 46 books in every cell. Your testes or ovaries can choose any combination of 23 books to put into each sperm or egg cell. That means that different sperm or eggs are likely to contain different sets of instructions.

How are twins made?

Twins are babies who grow, develop and are born at the same time. There are two types. Identical twins look exactly the same as each other. Non-identical twins look different from each other.

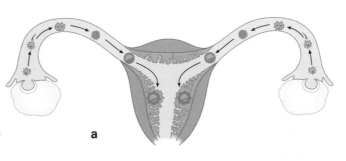

a

a   Non-identical twins are made when the woman releases two eggs at once, one from each ovary. Because sperm cells swim into each oviduct, each egg gets fertilised, and develops into a baby. Because different sperm and egg cells contain different instructions, the twins look different from each other.

b   **Identical twins** are made when an embryo splits accidentally in two. The cells in both embryos continue to divide. The embryos implant themselves into the uterus wall separately, and grow and develop into two separate babies. Because both embryos began with the same set of instructions (in the zygote), the twins look identical.

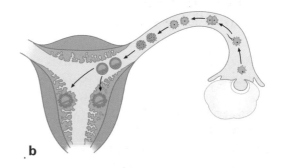

b

QUESTIONS

1 What happens immediately after fertilisation?

2 How many eggs have been fertilised if:

   a) non-identical twins are produced?

   b) identical twins are produced?

3 Why do sperm cells and egg cells only have a half set of instructions in their nucleus?

4 Explain why sisters or brothers are not usually identical, even though they have the same parents.

THE MENSTRUAL CYCLE

TOPIC CHECKLIST

- What is the menstrual cycle?
- How many babies can be made at once?
- What controls ovulation and menstruation?

What is the menstrual cycle?

When a girl is born, she has thousands of eggs stored in her **ovaries**. Between the ages of about 10 and 14, a girl's ovaries start to release those eggs into her oviducts. This process is called **ovulation**. One egg matures and is released from the ovaries every twenty-eight days.

a **How many eggs are usually released by a woman's ovaries in a whole year?**

Girls do not all start releasing eggs at the same age. Most girls start between 10 and 14, but some may start earlier or later.

Not every woman releases an egg exactly once every twenty-eight days. This is especially true in girls and young women.

If the egg gets fertilised in the oviduct, the uterus must be ready to receive the developing embryo.

- The uterus wall develops a thick lining, made of lots of blood vessels.
- When the fertilised egg reaches the uterus, it can implant itself into this lining.
- When this has happened, no more eggs are released until after the baby has been born.

If the egg is not fertilised within about three days, it dies, the uterus lining breaks down and passes, with the egg, through the cervix and out of the vagina. We call this **menstruation**, and say a woman is having her **period**. Once the uterus lining has passed out of the body, another egg begins to ripen before being released from the ovary. This process of ripening is called **maturation**. When maturation starts, the uterus lining also starts to build up again and the whole cycle repeats again.

We call this the **menstrual cycle**.

How many babies can be made at once?

Normally, only one egg matures and is released each month.
This means the woman's body can only produce one baby at a time.
As we saw in the last section, women do sometimes have twins, although this is quite rare.

b **How many eggs are released from the ovaries when non-identical twins are made?**

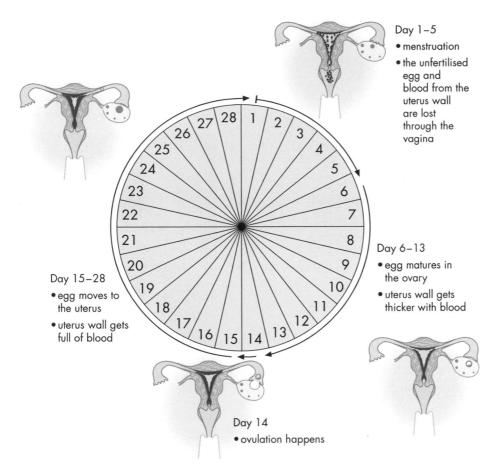

Day 1–5
- menstruation
- the unfertilised egg and blood from the uterus wall are lost through the vagina

Day 6–13
- egg matures in the ovary
- uterus wall gets thicker with blood

Day 15–28
- egg moves to the uterus
- uterus wall gets full of blood

Day 14
- ovulation happens

What controls ovulation and menstruation?

Hormones are chemicals which travel through the blood from one organ to another carrying messages. Hormones control when maturation, ovulation and menstruation happen. These hormones can also affect how a woman feels at different points in her cycle, and may make her feel tense immediately before her period.

c Explain why this tense feeling is sometimes called pre-menstrual tension (PMT).

QUESTIONS

1 What do these words mean?

  a) ovulation

  b) menstruation

2 What does *implant* mean?

3 a) What happens to the menstrual cycle if the egg is fertilised in the oviduct?

  b) How does a woman know if she is pregnant?

4 a) If a woman has a regular 28 day cycle, and her period begins on the 1st May, on what date would she next ovulate?

  b) How many egg cells does a woman usually produce each month?

  c) On what day of the menstrual cycle does a woman begin to menstruate?

PREGNANCY

What is pregnancy?

Once an egg has been fertilised, and has implanted itself in the uterus lining, the menstrual cycle stops. The uterus lining must not pass out of the body, or it would take the developing embryo with it.

When a woman is carrying an embryo, she is pregnant. The embryo grows and develops over a period of about nine months before it is born. This period of nine months is called the **gestation period**.

a **What is the advantage of keeping the child in the mother's body for nine months of pregnancy?**

What is the placenta?

In the uterus wall, the embryo needs food and oxygen to survive, but it cannot eat or breathe like we do. The mother's blood carries food and oxygen, and the embryo must absorb them from the blood vessels in the uterus wall.

b **Why does the embryo need food and oxygen?**

As it grows, the embryo needs more and more food and oxygen. It also needs to get rid of carbon dioxide and waste materials (it cannot breathe out, or go to the toilet!). To help achieve this, a special organ develops: the **placenta**.

The placenta joins the baby to the mother. Blood vessels from the mother and blood vessels from the embryo pass very close to each other in the placenta, but their blood does not mix.

The mother's and embryo's blood vessels are so close that food and oxygen can pass from the mother's blood into the embryo's blood. Carbon dioxide and other waste materials can also pass from the embryo's blood into the mother's blood. The mother gets rid of these from her body.

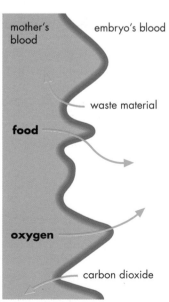

What happens inside the placenta

If a mother is not careful during pregnancy, she can damage her baby. If the mother's blood has anything harmful in it, this may travel across the placenta into the embryo's blood. Because of this, women should not smoke or drink alcohol during pregnancy. These can slow down the growth of a baby.

Pregnant mothers must also avoid catching German measles (*Rubella*). This disease makes poisons which can get across the placenta into the baby's blood, causing mental and physical damage.

c **Why are teenage girls vaccinated against German measles?**

After about eight weeks, the embryo is too big to stay in the uterus wall. It is then called a **fetus**, and floats free in a bag of **amniotic fluid** in the uterus.

This fluid protects it from getting damaged; it supports the fetus and acts like a shock absorber. The fetus is still attached to the placenta by the **umbilical cord**, and continues to grow. The umbilical cord takes the baby's blood to the placenta and back again.

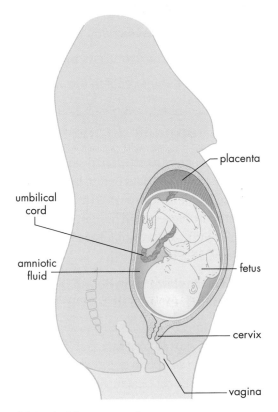

A fetus inside a pregnant woman

QUESTIONS

1 What does the word *pregnant* mean?

2 Arrange these words in the correct order to show how a fetus gets rid of waste from its cells.
fetus's cells, mother's blood, umbilical cord, placenta.

3 When is a developing baby called:

   a) an embryo?

   b) a fetus?

4 During pregnancy, a woman's behaviour may change. By thinking about the effect of the fetus on its mother, explain:

   a) why the mother may need to eat more

   b) why the mother may go to the toilet more often

WHAT DO NEWBORN BABIES NEED?

TOPIC CHECKLIST

- What happens during birth?
- What happens if a baby is born early?
- Why do human mothers make milk?
- How do babies react to the world?

What happens during birth?

About nine months after fertilisation, the baby is ready to be born. In the few days before **birth**, the baby turns so that its head is facing downwards (**a**). This is so that its head, which is the biggest, and hardest part of its body can force its way out first. Occasionally, babies are born bottom first; this is called a 'breech birth'.

ⓐ **Which type of birth do you think is the easiest: head first or bottom first?**

Birth is a long process. It begins when the muscles in the uterus wall start to **contract**, pulling the wall of the uterus upwards and so opening the cervix (**b**). While this is happening, the cervical muscles also begin to relax. When the **contractions** have started, people say the mother is 'in **labour**'. The contractions can last for a long time and are often very painful, but the mother is helped by a midwife or doctor.

Once the cervix is about 10cm wide, the contractions in the uterus change, pushing the baby down (**c**). At this point, or before, the bag of fluid around the baby bursts and the fluid passes out of the mother through the vagina. People sometimes call this the '**waters breaking**'.

Eventually, the baby is pushed out of the uterus.through the vagina, and out of the mother's body (**d**). The umbilical cord is clamped in two places and cut between the clamps.

ⓑ **Why do you think the umbilical cord is clamped before it is cut?**

About 20 minutes after birth, the placenta passes out of the vagina with the remains of the umbilical cord attached. This is often called the **afterbirth**.

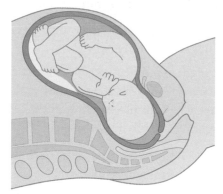

a

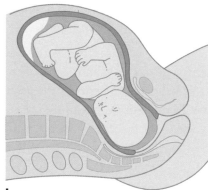

b

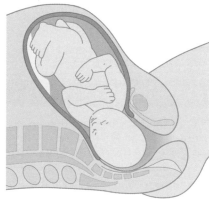

c

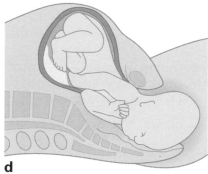

d

What happens if a baby is born early?

If the baby is born early, we say it is **premature**. To help it finish developing, doctors put it in an incubator. Inside an incubator, conditions are very similar to those inside the mother's uterus. For example, the temperature is the same, there are no diseases, and food is put directly into the baby's blood (through a tube called a 'drip').

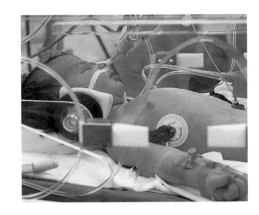

C Why do conditions inside the incubator need to be the same as inside the uterus?

Why do human mothers make milk?

A mother's breasts (**mammary glands**) produce milk for the baby to feed on. This makes sure her baby gets a constant supply of food and water. The table shows the types of food contained in the milk.

The mother's milk also contains antibodies against diseases. These are chemicals which are normally found in the mother's blood. They help the baby to kill bacteria and viruses which may get into its blood. This stops them making the baby ill.

Type of food	Why does the baby need it?
Fat	Energy
	Growth of the brain
Sugar	Energy
Protein	Growth
Calcium	Growth of bones

How do babies react to the world?

At birth, a baby enters a completely new and confusing world. It relies on its mother to look after it. However, to help it survive in these early stages, it does have reflex actions. A reflex is an instinctive kind of behaviour designed to protect the baby. For example, if you touch a baby's cheek, it will turn its head towards you, looking for a breast to feed from.

QUESTIONS

1 What is the afterbirth? What was its job?

2 a) What types of food are contained in human milk?

  b) What is each type of food used for?

3 List three ways in which humans care for their children after birth.

4 Some babies are fed on bottled milk. What effect may this have on a baby's health?

HOW DO HUMANS CHANGE AS THEY GROW?

How do children grow?

Growth is an increase in size. Most scientists measure growth by looking at peoples' height or mass.

Human growth occurs in spurts. At some ages humans grow quickly while at other ages humans grow slowly. Boys and girls have growth spurts at slightly different times in their life.

Remember, growth happens when new cells are made by cell division. In adolescence, cells divide very quickly to make lots of new cells. In adulthood, new cells are only made at the same speed that old cells are dying.

This graph shows how people grow, on average, during their lifetime. Don't worry if you are larger or smaller than the graph says you should be. There is nothing wrong with this; people vary a great deal in how much and how fast they grow at different ages. If we all grew at the same speed at the same time, we would all look like a race of robots!

ⓐ **Between what ages are girls, on average, larger than boys?**

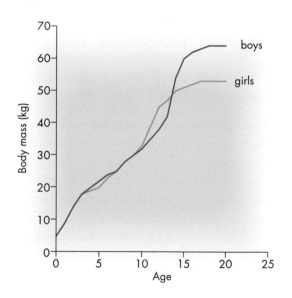

How do children develop?

Children **develop** when they change physically and emotionally. These changes allow them to survive on their own and reproduce. Most of these changes happen during a period called **adolescence**.

Boys and girls change in different ways during adolescence, and at different ages. Girls normally start to change before boys, although most changes happen in both sexes between the ages of 10 and 18.

Physical changes

Physical changes normally begin to happen before emotional changes, and are triggered by hormones released from the brain. The reproductive organs increase in size and begin to produce gametes, and a person's appearance begins to change. The changes in physical appearance are called **secondary sexual characteristics**. Many of these make a person more attractive to the opposite sex. These physical changes occur during the part of adolescence called **puberty**.

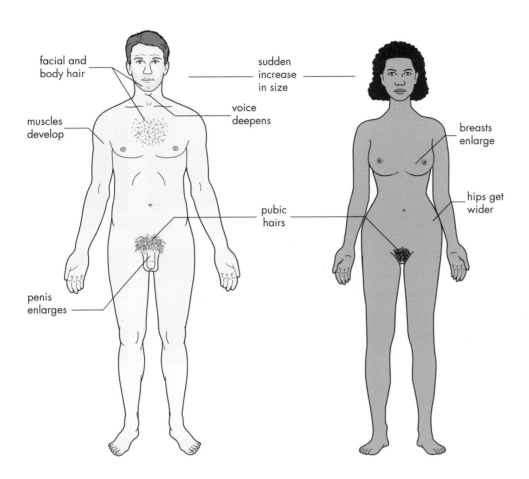

facial and body hair

muscles develop

penis enlarges

sudden increase in size

voice deepens

pubic hairs

breasts enlarge

hips get wider

Emotional changes

The hormones which affect physical changes can also affect people emotionally as well. Their behaviour and mood may alter a lot and they may easily become angry, upset or depressed. During adolescence, a child's way of thinking will also start to change. These changes will eventually help the child to survive on its own when it becomes an adult.

QUESTIONS

1 What is growth, and what is it caused by?

2 List five changes which happen in boys and girls during adolescence.

3 What is the difference between adolescence and puberty?

4 If changes in appearance during adolescence are called secondary sexual characteristics, what do you think primary sexual characteristics are?

C Environment and feeding relationships

C1 ADAPTING TO THE ENVIRONMENT

TOPIC CHECKLIST

- Why are habitats different from each other?
- Why do different organisms live in different habitats?

Why are habitats different from each other?

The place where an animal or plant lives is called its **habitat**. Different animals and plants live in different habitats, but what makes the habitats different in the first place?

Habitats have different **temperatures**: some are cold, and some are hot. They also have different amounts of light. In a desert the Sun's light and heat are very strong, but in the depths of an ocean there is very little light and it is very cold. These different conditions are called **environmental factors**.

ⓐ Look at the pictures of different habitats. For each habitat, write down the environmental factors there.

Arctic

Woodland

Desert

Underwater

Why do different organisms live in different habitats?

The environmental conditions in a habitat affect what lives there. In any habitat you will find only plants and animals with features which help them cope with the conditions there. We say they are **adapted** to living there.

Living in water

- Fish live in ponds, rivers or in the sea. They have fins and a tail to push them through the water, and a **streamlined** shape, which helps them to move through the water easily.

- Because they live in water, fish cannot breathe air like we do. Instead they have **gills** which take the oxygen out of the water.

Plants also live in water. Look at the picture of the water-lilies. Water-lilies live in ponds which are often very murky. How do they cope with this?

- They have long stems which reach up towards the light. The leaves at the end of the stems float on the surface of the water where they get a lot of light to help them make food.

- They have flowers which also float on the surface of the water. Flying insects can land on the flowers and take pollen from one to the other, helping the lilies to reproduce.

Living underground

Moles live underground in long tunnels which they dig themselves.

- They have a thick coat of fur to keep them warm.

- They have big front feet which they use for digging. They also have a streamlined shape to help them squeeze through tunnels.

- They have poor eyesight. Because it is dark underground, they don't need good eyes. Instead, they have a brilliant sense of smell, and a good sense of touch. They can even detect vibrations coming through the soil!

Living in woodland

Blackbirds live in gardens and in woodland.

- They have large wings and a wide tail. These help them fly between the trees and change direction quickly.

- They have very detailed colour vision which helps them find food on the trees and on the woodland floor.

- They have a streamlined shape which helps them move through the air.

- They have grasping claws which help them perch on the branches.

Plants also live in woodland. Some plants (like ivy) climb up others to get to the light. Other smaller plants grow and flower early, like the bluebells in this wood. This means they get light to make food before the leaves of the bigger trees grow and block out the light.

QUESTIONS

1 a What is a habitat?

b Write down three environmental factors which can be different in different habitats.

2 Describe two ways in which plants are adapted to cope with the lack of light in a wood.

3 Explain five ways in which a mole is adapted to living underground.

4 Why do you think colour vision helps blackbirds to find their food in a woodland?

5 Design an imaginary animal which is adapted to living in the desert *and* to living underground. You can combine adaptations from lots of different animals in the same imaginary animal.

ADAPTING TO DAILY CHANGES IN THE ENVIRONMENT

How does a habitat change every day?

Your school grounds are home to lots of different animals and plants. Even if you don't have a school field, look at the walls, the cracks between the paving slabs, or the trees. There are lots of plants and animals living in all these places. Your school is their habitat. But their habitat changes every day in lots of ways.

Noise levels

Every morning at about nine o'clock, the school is noisy as students arrive. In lesson time, the school goes fairly quiet. During break and lunch times, the school is noisy and after four o'clock, the school goes quiet again.

Light intensity and temperature

In the early morning, the Sun rises. The light from the Sun is weak, but as it keeps rising in the sky, the light gets stronger. The heat from the Sun also gets stronger as the day goes on, even in the winter.

When the Sun sets, the sky grows darker and it starts to get colder. As the night goes on, it gets colder and colder without the Sun's rays.

We call the strength of light its **intensity**. You can measure light intensity with a light probe. Just as you measure distance in units called centimetres, you measure light intensity in units called **lux**. The graph shows changes in light intensity over 24 hours.

ⓐ Using the graph, say what time it got dark on this day.

ⓑ Using the graph, say what time it starts to get light.

ⓒ When was the light most intense?

Wet and dry

Not all changes happen at a regular time every day. It could rain at any time: day or night!

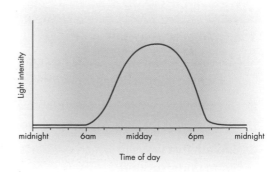

How are living things adapted to daily changes in their habitat?

Animals and plants are adapted to changes in environmental conditions. Crows, starlings and squirrels only visit schools when they are quiet. When it is quiet, they are unlikely to be in any danger. They are adapted to avoiding danger.

d **Can you think of any other reasons why they come to school immediately after break and lunch times?**

Some animals, such as foxes, slugs, cats and mice, only become active when it gets dark. If you stayed in school all night, you would probably see some of them. Animals which are active at night, are called **nocturnal**. Those which are active during the day, are called **diurnal**.

Butterflies shelter from the rain to stop their wings getting wet. If their wings get wet they cannot fly! So even though they are diurnal, you still won't see them on a wet day.

Plants also respond to changes in light intensity. Most flowers are open during the day to allow pollination and then close at night for protection.

You can investigate in the lab how animals respond to changes in environmental conditions. The picture on the right shows a choice chamber. It is called a choice chamber because it gives woodlice a choice of where to go.

The filter paper on the left of the dish is damp, and the paper on the right is dry. By measuring how long woodlice spend on each side of the chamber, you can see how moisture affects their activity.

damp filter paper   dry filter paper

A choice chamber

e **Explain how you could change the choice chamber to investigate the effect of light intensity on woodlice.**

QUESTIONS

1 a Give two ways in which changes in the environment can alter what an animal does during a particular day.

b Give one way in which changes in the environment can alter what a plant does during a particular day.

2 Give one way in which *you* respond to changes in these environmental conditions during a particular day: **a** light intensity **b** temperature **c** rainfall.

3 A night is usually coldest just before the sun rises at dawn. Why?

4 Joachim used the choice chamber to investigate the effect of moisture on woodlice activity. He used only one woodlouse, and put one side of the chamber facing the window. Explain **a** whether his experiment was reliable and fair, and **b** how he could have improved his experimental design.

ADAPTING TO YEARLY CHANGES IN THE ENVIRONMENT

TOPIC CHECKLIST

- Why do living things change during the year?
- How are living things adapted to yearly changes in their habitat?

Why do living things change during the year?

You do things differently in the summer and the winter.

- In winter, you wear a thicker coat and spend more time inside.
- In summer you wear shorts, and spend lots of time outside.

Your environment changes during the year, and you change your behaviour to cope with these changes.

Look at the pairs of pictures of these four habitats in the winter and the summer.

Garden

Woodland

Arctic

Seashore

a **Write down two differences between the pictures of each habitat.**

Changes in living things during the year normally happen in response to changes in environmental conditions like temperature, light intensity, availability of food and availability of water.

How are living things adapted to yearly changes in their habitat?

Wildebeest live in Africa and feed on grass. Grass can only grow where it rains, and wildebeest travel hundreds of miles across Africa every winter looking for places with lots of grass. This is called **migration**.

Wildebeest migration

Some insects spend the winter living inside a protective case called a pupa. A pupa is a **dormant structure** which protects them from the extreme winter weather. Inside the pupa, their life processes slow down, and they only emerge in the summer when conditions are better.

Butterfly emerging from a pupa

Plants also make dormant structures. For example, in the winter, some plants store food in their roots, stems or leaves under the soil. The part of the plant above the ground dies in the cold. The part containing the stored food only starts to grow again when conditions are good enough.

Dormant structures in plants

Sometimes, the whole plant becomes dormant. In winter in the UK, light intensity is very low. This means there is not much light for plants to make food so some trees save their energy by losing their leaves. This means they do not grow, but keep alive using their stored food.

Because plants die off or lose their leaves, there is not much plant food available in the winter for animals. Squirrels cope with this by storing nuts in the autumn to eat in the winter months.

Some animals, like tortoises, hedgehogs and bears, cannot store enough food to keep them going. Instead, they go to sleep in a warm sheltered place, such as under a pile of old leaves or inside an old tree trunk. This is called **hibernation**.

Some animals get a thicker coat in the winter to keep them warm. They lose it (they **moult**) in the summer or they would get too warm. Most cats and dogs moult in the summer.

QUESTIONS

1 How do environmental conditions change between winter and summer in this country?

2 Describe five ways in which animals change their behaviour to cope with the winter.

3 Describe four ways in which living things may become dormant.

PREDATORS AND PREY

TOPIC CHECKLIST

- Finding food
- What are predators and prey?
- Why are predators good at hunting for food?
- How do prey avoid being eaten?

Finding food

Changes in seasons and the weather are not the only important factors in an animal's habitat. If there is no food available, animals will not survive!

All animals are adapted to getting food. Birds have beaks of different shapes and sizes, depending on what they eat. Their beak is adapted to what they eat.

Zebra finches

Hawfinch

Eagle

a **Which of these birds has the best beak to eat small seeds, large seeds and other animals?**

What are predators and prey?

Animals eat either plants or other animals. If they hunt for and eat other animals they are called **predators**. The animals they hunt and kill are called **prey**.

A lion is a predator which hunts for and kills zebras and antelopes. They are the lion's prey. An eagle is a predator which hunts and kills prey like mice and rabbits.

A cow is not a predator because it does not hunt for and kill another animal. It eats grass instead. Grass is not prey. Only animals are prey.

Predators

Prey

Why are predators good at hunting for food?

Look at the pictures of predators below. They all look quite fierce and frightening. They look like this because they have adaptations which make them good at hunting and killing other animals.

The adaptations of a predator

This kestrel has excellent eyesight. It also has eyes pointing forwards which makes it easier to judge distance and so catch its prey.

A good sense of smell makes it easier for an anteater to sniff out its prey.

The lion's sharp claws and teeth make it easier to attack and kill its prey. Many bird predators have hooked beaks which do the same job.

Spiders lie in wait until a fly gets trapped in their web!

Many predators have a colour or pattern similar to their surroundings. This is called camouflage.

ⓑ Many predators have more than one adaptation to help them catch food. Think about a crocodile and a snake. Write down two adaptations in each animal which help it hunt for food.

How do prey avoid being eaten?

The adaptations of prey

Having eyes at the side helps this rabbit watch out for predators all around it. It also has big ears and a good sense of smell.

Hares run fast and are easily startled. A quick exit may save their life.

Like some predators, some prey have camouflage.

This tortoise has built in protection!

Some prey have weapons to defend themselves.

QUESTIONS

1 Look at the list of plants and animals, and answer the questions which follow: oak tree; mouse; eagle; grass; zebra; dog; pike; bat; wolf; shark.

a Which of these are (i) predators, (ii) prey, (iii) neither predators nor prey?

b Choose one of the predators. Write down two features which make it good at hunting for and killing its prey.

c Choose one of the prey. Write down two features which make it good at avoiding being caught and eaten.

2 Most predators are active during the day. Try to explain why some prey species are nocturnal.

C5 FOOD CHAINS AND FOOD WEBS

TOPIC CHECKLIST

- Where do plants and animals get their food?
- What is a food chain?
- What do food webs tell us?

Where do plants and animals get their food?

Plants produce their own food using energy from the Sun and so are called **producers**. Animals are **consumers** because they must consume (eat) other living things for food. Animals which only eat plants are called **herbivores**. Animals which only eat other animals are called **carnivores**. Animals which eat both plants and other animals are called **omnivores**.

What is a food chain?

A rabbit eats grass and a fox eats the rabbit. They form a **food chain**. A food chain starts with a plant, shows the animal which eats the plant, and then shows the animal which eats this animal, and so on. We can draw it like this:

grass ⟶ rabbit ⟶ fox

ⓐ **Write out all the food chains which you can see in the picture of the meadow.**

ⓑ **Make a list of the producers, carnivores and herbivores in the picture.**

There are special names for the consumers.

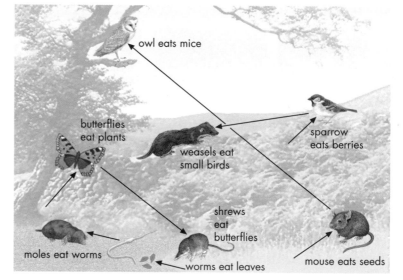

owl eats mice

butterflies eat plants

weasels eat small birds

sparrow eats berries

shrews eat butterflies

moles eat worms

worms eat leaves

mouse eats seeds

- The rabbit is the first consumer in the chain. It is called the **primary consumer**; the primary consumer eats the producer.

- The fox is the second consumer in the chain. It is called the **secondary consumer**; the secondary consumer eats the primary consumer.

A food chain doesn't just show what eats what. It also shows how **energy** is passed between members of the food chain.

- The grass uses energy from the Sun to make food; it stores this energy in its body.

- When the rabbit eats the grass, it gets the energy, uses some, and stores the rest in its body.

- When the fox eats the rabbit, it gets the energy, uses some, and stores the rest in its body.

The arrows show the direction in which energy flows through the food chain.

What do food webs tell us?

There is normally more than one food chain in each habitat. Most animals and plants are part of more than one food chain. For example, many different herbivores eat grass and some of these herbivores are eaten by more than one carnivore. To show this, we draw a **food web**.

Drawing a food web is more useful than just drawing lots of separate food chains. Food webs let us see how energy flows through all the living things in a habitat. We can see which animals are competing against each other for food, and which other animals would be affected if one kind of animal were to die out suddenly or reduce in numbers.

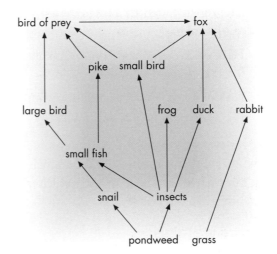

c Look at the food web. Write down two animals which compete with each other for food.

d What would happen to the number of rabbits if all the foxes died out?

QUESTIONS

1 What do these words mean?
  a carnivore; **b** herbivore; **c** consumer; **d** producer.

2 Why do food chains always start with a producer?

3 Cats eat robins. Robins eat slugs. Slugs eat broccoli.

  a Draw a food chain to show these feeding relationships.

  b What do the arrows in the food chain show?

4 Foxes eat beetles, rats and rabbits. Owls eat beetles, rats and rabbits. Stoats eat rats and rabbits. Plant leaves are eaten by beetles, rats and rabbits.

  a Draw a food web to show these feeding relationships.

  b Which organisms compete with each other for food ?

  c What would happen to the number of beetles if all the rabbits died out?

5 Think of where you live. Write down at least two food chains you can see around you (include people and pets!).

C6 FOOD WEB DETECTIVES

TOPIC CHECKLIST

- How do you know what lives in a habitat?
- How do you work out what eats what?
- How do plants avoid being eaten by animals?

How do you know what lives in a habitat?

You can probably identify a lot of the animals and plants in your garden or local park. But is your knowledge good enough?

- Have you definitely seen *all* the plants and animals which live there?
- Do you know what every plant and animal is called?
- Do you know what each animal eats?

The easiest way to answer these questions is to go outside and look! You probably see most of the animals and plants every day. But what about those animals which try to hide away? Here are some ways to reveal them!

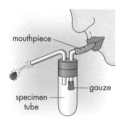

Pooters: Have a close look at the plants and trees. Suck up any animals you can find into the tube.

Tree beating: Spread a big sheet out under a tree. Shake the branches and see which animals fall onto the sheet.

Pit-fall traps: After a few hours, you should find a little group of unsuspecting insects in the bottom!

Sweep netting: If your garden has long grass, sweep the net backwards and forwards. Any insects get knocked off the grass and into your net.

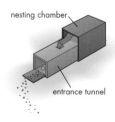

Small mammal traps: Put a trail of bait leading into the trap. If an animal goes in, the door will close behind it. Make sure you check the traps regularly or the animal may die of cold.

How do you work out what eats what?

So we know *what* lives in the garden or park. But remember, we want to draw a food web to show which organisms eat each other. To find out what eats what, we need some clues! Look at the pictures to see the kind of clues we could use.

Owl droppings are solid pellets. If you break open owl droppings, you can sometimes recognise parts of the animals which have been eaten by the owl.

If you find a dead animal or bones under an eagle's nest, you can be fairly sure the eagle ate the animal which they came from.

Thrushes pick up snails in their beak and break the shell against a stone to get at the flesh inside. If you ever see a smashed snail shell, you know who has eaten it.

The woodlouse wouldn't be on the wood, unless it was going to use it for food.

ⓐ Who is eating the leaves from the rose bush?

ⓑ Can you work out who has made the teeth marks in the chocolate?

ⓓ Whose lunch is this?

ⓒ If you found purple bird droppings, what might the bird have eaten?

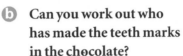

How do plants avoid being eaten by animals?

Animals and plants often have special adaptations to stop animals eating them. We have already seen the animals' adaptations earlier in this chapter. Plants may have stings or spikes to stop animals eating them.

QUESTIONS

1 a How do you use a pooter?

  b When would you use a sweep net?

2 You want to know what an eagle eats. What evidence could you use to find out?

3 You are an alien and you arrive on Earth from outer space. What evidence could you use to find out what humans eat?

D Variation and classification

VARIATION

What is variation?

Some types of living things look very alike. For example, two dogs look very alike, two cats look very alike and two humans look very alike. But each dog looks very different from each human, each cat looks very different from each dog, and each human looks very different from each cat. In other words, they vary a lot. We say there is a lot of **variation** between them.

However, all cats don't look the same, all dogs don't look the same and all humans don't look the same. There is variation between them. Look at the pictures of dogs.

Here are some of the ways in which they look different from each other:

- hair colour ● hair length ● ear size ● height ● mass

There is not just variation between dogs. Look at the pictures of the snails and daisies.

Snails   Daisies

a Write down three ways in which snails are different from each other.

b Write down three ways in which daisies are different from each other.

How do you draw graphs of variation?

You can use graphs to show how animals or plants are different from each other. For example, students in 9WM at King Edward School decided to find out how their eye colour and heights varied. They recorded their results in a tally chart, and drew two graphs.

	Eye colour		
	Blue	Brown	Green
Tally	ＨＨＴ ＨＨＴ ｜｜	ＨＨＴ ＨＨＴ	｜｜｜｜
Total	12	10	4

	Height				
	140.0 - 149.9	150.0 - 159.9	160.0 - 169.9	170.0 - 179.9	180.0 - 189.9
Tally	ＨＨＴ	ＨＨＴ ＨＨＴ	ＨＨＴ ｜｜	｜｜｜｜	
Total	5	10	7	4	0

In both graphs, the class put people into groups:

- With eye colour, the group was already there, e.g. blue, green or brown.

- With height, they had to describe each group before they could put people into them.

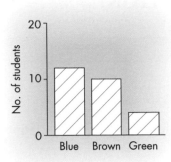

Eye colour

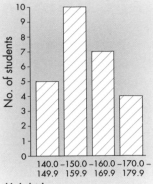

Height in cm

c What is the most common eye colour?

d What is the most common height?

You can also use graphs to answer particular questions about variation. For example, do pink tipped daisies have longer stems? To find the answer, don't try to look at *all* the daisies in a field or garden, just look at a sample of about twenty.

You need to find the average length of pink tipped daisies' stems, and the average length of normal daisies' stems. Look at the table to see how to work this out.

	Pink - tipped daisies	Normal daisies
Total no. of daisies	10	10
Stem length of each daisy (mm)	12, 14, 13, 10, 11,14, 13, 9, 15, 13	15, 9, 10, 11, 10, 11, 12, 9, 9, 10
Total stem length of all daisies (mm)	124	106
Average stem length of a daisy (mm)	12.4	10.6

e **Draw a graph with these results to show whether pink-tipped daisies have longer stems.**

Average stem length of a daisy = Total stem length of all daisies ÷ Total number of daisies

The graphs below contain information about variation in snails and in holly. Use them to answer the questions.

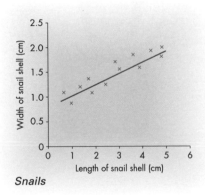

Snails

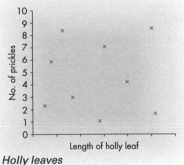

Holly leaves

f **Do snails with longer shells have wider shells?**

g **Do longer holly leaves have more prickles?**

QUESTIONS

1 Write down ten ways in which humans are different from each other.

2 Write down five ways in which **a)** dogs and **b)** cats, can be different from each other.

3 Look at the data below about shoe size.

   a Draw a graph to show how many people have each shoe size.

   b What is (i) the most common shoe size and (ii) the least common shoe size?

Shoe size	2	3	4	5	6	7	8	9
Number of people	1	2	4	6	7	5	2	1

WHAT CAUSES VARIATION?

TOPIC CHECKLIST

- What is inherited variation?
- What is environmental variation?
- How do the environment *and* inheritance affect variation?

What is inherited variation?

Have you ever been told that you have your mother's eyes, or your father's nose? Children often look a little like their parents because some of their parents' features were passed onto them. They **inherited** those features from their parents.

Children never look exactly like either of their parents, and brothers and sisters rarely look exactly the same. This is because each child inherits a different mixture of features from both parents. This type of variation is called **inherited variation**.

Look at the family tree.

- Each child has inherited their hair colour from one of their parents.

- Each child has inherited their hair type (curly or straight) from one of their parents.

Both boys *and* girls can inherit features from their mother *and* from their father. In this case, the boy has inherited curly hair from his mum, and big ears from his dad.

a Where did the girl inherit her blue eyes from?

b Why does no-one ever look exactly like either of their parents?

Both plants and animals can inherit features from their parents. Good examples of inherited variation in plants include flower colour and leaf shape.

What is environmental variation?

The only time that brothers and sisters look identical is when they are identical twins. Identical twins inherit the same features from their parents. When they are born, they look exactly the same.

However, identical twins can look different from each other as they get older. This is not because they inherited different features, but because their features have been changed by their surroundings or environment. This is called **environmental variation**.

Environmental variation can be caused not only by a living thing's surroundings, but by what it eats, what it drinks, and how it lives. All animals and plants are affected by environmental variation.

For example, a person who goes weight-training will have larger muscles than someone who does not train.

Plants which live in the shade will grow taller than plants which live in the sun, so they can reach the light more easily.

Plant kept in the sun *Plant kept in the shade*

c **The differences in the pictures of the nettles and trees have been caused by the environment. Suggest what may have caused these differences.**

How do the environment *and* inheritance affect variation?

A lot of features can be affected both by inheritance and by the environment. Imagine a person who has inherited the following features from their mother:

- tall ● thin ● athletic

Their environment can still affect these features:

- They will not be tall unless they eat a good, balanced diet.
- They will not be thin if they eat lots of fatty food.
- They will not be athletic unless they train a lot.

Nettles

Trees

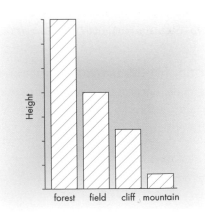

QUESTIONS

1 What are the two causes of variation in living things?

2 Which of these types of variation are caused by (a) inheritance, (b) the environment, and (c) both? accent; natural hair colour; nose shape; eye colour; mass; blood group; curly hair; height

3 The graph shows the average height of oak trees growing in different places. Suggest three environmental conditions which stop trees growing tall.

(Bar graph: Height vs location — forest, field, cliff, mountain)

HOW CAN WE DESCRIBE LIVING THINGS?

TOPIC CHECKLIST

- How do you write about the differences between living things?
- How do you describe accurately the differences between living things?

How do you write about the differences between living things?

Different animals and plants look and behave very differently. There is a lot of variation between them.

There are lots of ways to describe living things. Look at these descriptions of a horse.

This breed is compact, strong and muscular, with a large but well-shaped head. They have short cannon bones, big knees and hocks. They are intelligent and well-behaved, making them easy to train. The colour at birth is usually grey, brown or black, changing to white over the first five years.

Reference Guide

Round-hoof'd, short-jointed, ... full eye, small head, and nostril wide,
High crest, short ears, straight legs and passing strong,
Thin mane, thick tail, broad buttock, tender hide:
Look what a horse should have he did not lack
Save a proud rider on so proud a back.

from Venus and Adonis *by Shakespeare*

...she stood like a statue, watching, her head very high, clean-cut in profile, with a wide cheek and a forehead so broad that a brow band had had to be made specially for her. Her face tapered sharply to a delicate muzzle the colour of the underside of field mushrooms, pinky grey, soft and plushy. Now her nostrils were wide and her breath came quickly as she sniffed the air and listened to the shepherd whistling to his dog.

from Lost in the Moors *by Diana Pullein Thompson*

Writing like this may not describe an animal or plant perfectly. Look at the extract from the poem. It could easily be talking about a zebra rather than a horse. A zebra is a different animal from a horse.

a Why do you think these descriptions are so different?

b Which of these descriptions would a scientist like the most? Explain why.

How do you describe accurately the differences between living things?

To help someone tell the difference between two animals, you need to describe each animal's features accurately. You could count the number of each feature, measure its size or record its colour. You can record this information in a table like this one for a honeybee.

Body sections (segments)	Legs	Antennae	Wings	Tail
How many?	6	2	2 pairs	no
How big?	up to 1 cm	short	1 cm	—
What colour?	black	black	grey	—

The table will be different depending on what you are trying to identify. Look at the pictures of the fish.

c Which features could you use to tell the fish apart? Draw a table using these features as column headings, and fill in a copy of the table for each fish.

Of course, you do not need to stop only at what an animal looks like! Animals behave in different ways as well. For example, pigeons 'coo' while chickens 'cluck'.

QUESTIONS

1 Describe a cat by (i) writing a poem, and (ii) making a table about it.

2 An alien arrives on earth. They have never seen a cat before. Which description do you think they will find most useful?

3 Make a table to describe and compare yourself with any member of your family.

HOW CAN WE SORT LIVING THINGS INTO GROUPS?

TOPIC CHECKLIST

- What is classification?
- How do you classify living things?

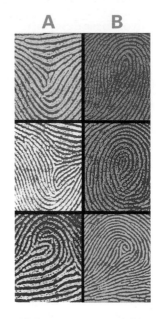

A   B

What is classification?

There are millions of living things in the world and to be able to recognise them more easily, scientists sort them into groups. This is called **classifying**.

But when almost every living thing is different from every other, how do you decide which ones go into which group? The answer is that you look for the features which they have in common. If two animals have a lot of features in common, they go into the same group. We can see how this works using human fingerprints.

Look at the fingerprints on the right. Fingerprints can be used to identify criminals because no-one (except identical twins) has the same fingerprint as anyone else.

Even though every fingerprint is different, they still have some features in common. Look at the way in which they have been sorted into two groups: A and B.

ⓐ **Draw the feature which all of group A have, but which all of group B do not have.**

How do you classify living things?

The fingerprints in the example above were all different. But you could still put them into groups. You did it by looking at the features which the fingerprints had in common. Those fingerprints which had features in common went into the same group.

You classify living things in exactly the same way. Scientists put living things into groups, depending on how many features they have in common. These groups are called taxonomic groups because the scientific name for classification is **taxonomy**.

ⓑ **Sort these animals into two groups. Explain which features you have used to decide which animal goes into which group. No animal can be in both groups.**

Horse

Impala

Wildebeest

Haartebeest

Oryx

Zebra

Living things which have almost all their features in common are members of a group called a **species**. Examples of different species include humans, dogs and cats.

Just because a group of animals has one feature in common, it does not mean they will have all their other features in common. Because of this, two people may divide animals up into groups in different ways. This will happen if they look at different features when deciding on their groups.

QUESTIONS

1 Look at the pictures of leaves on the right. Classify them into two groups and explain which of their features you used to group them together.

2 a Divide the animals in the picture above into two groups. Write down the feature(s) you used to group them together.

   b Divide them into two different groups. Use a different feature to group them together.

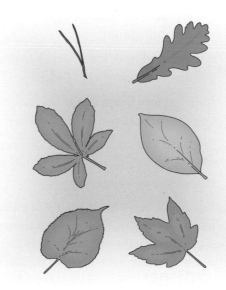

WHY DO SCIENTISTS CLASSIFY LIVING THINGS?

Why do humans put things into groups?

Humans like classifying. We often classify objects without even noticing. But there is normally a good reason for it!

Nails and screws look very similar (they have a flat head and a long shaft) and do the same job (they join things together), but they look different and do their job in different ways. Because of this, we classify them into two groups.

● We call some of them nails because they have smooth shafts, and we hammer them into things.

● We call some of them screws because they have a winding thread, and we twist them into things.

ⓐ Can you think of any other pairs of household objects which look very similar, but are given different names?

Why do scientists classify living things?

Just as with nails, there are special reasons why scientists put living things into groups.

1 If they have lots of living things to think about, it lets them put them in some sort of order.

2 If they meet a living thing they have never met before, it helps them understand what that new species is like.

3 Scientists can work out how closely related two species are. If two species look very similar, they are probably closely related to each other.

4 It makes it easier for them to tell other scientists about a particular species. Think about the nails and screws again. If everyone in the world classifies them in the same way, using the same names, even a person who speaks a different language will understand what something looks like, and what it does, if you call it a 'six inch nail'.

Nails

Screws

Carl Linnaeus, a Swedish botanist, was the first person to realise this. He gave each species a name in Latin. Every species still has a Latin name today. By using the Latin name, scientists all over the world can be certain they are talking about the same species.

ⓑ **Why is it particularly important to use a living organism's Latin name in agriculture and medicine?**

How do scientists classify living things?

Between 384 and 322 BC, Aristotle, a famous Greek scientist, classified living things for the first time. He said that anything green was a plant, and anything that moved was an animal. He did not get this quite right because greenfly are animals.

In the nineteenth century, John Hogg divided up living things into three main groups: animals, plants and microbes. Microbes were any living thing which could only be seen using a microscope.

In the twentieth century, scientists have agreed to put all the species into large groups called **kingdoms**. Every species on the earth is a member of one of the five kingdoms. The two kingdoms you will learn about are animals and plants.

Animals

What is the difference between animals and plants?

If you had to describe the differences between animals and plants, what would you say?

The main difference between plants and animals is that plants make their own food using a green substance called **chlorophyll**. Animals, on the other hand, have to eat plants or other animals to get food. To help them find the food, animals can also move from one place to another.

Plants

QUESTIONS

1 Give four reasons for classifying living things.

2 Write down the names of three scientists who worked on classification. What did each of them say about classifying living things?

3 Into which kingdom would you classify the following species?
   a lion; **b** oak tree; **c** human; **d** daffodil.

4 Latin was the language used in ancient Rome and medieval Europe. No-one speaks it anymore, so why is it so useful for naming species today?

HOW DO SCIENTISTS CLASSIFY ANIMALS?

How can you divide the animal kingdom into smaller groups?

Each kingdom can be split into more than one group. The animal kingdom is split into two groups called **vertebrates** and **invertebrates**. Vertebrates have a backbone and invertebrates do not have a backbone.

How can you divide vertebrates into smaller groups?

Vertebrates can be divided into five groups. All the members of each group have features in common. Look at the diagrams to find out what those features are.

Fish: Gills, fins, scales, streamlined body, live in water.

Amphibians: Soft, wet skin, lungs, live in water or on land.

Birds: Feathers, lungs, wings, lay eggs with a shell.

Mammals: Hair or fur, lungs, babies develop inside mother, babies fed on milk from the mother.

Reptiles: Dry skin covered in scales, lungs, lay eggs with a shell, live on land.

How can you divide invertebrates into smaller groups?

Invertebrates can also be divided into smaller groups. Look at the table to see the common features of some of these groups.

Annelids – long body divided into rings, bristles called chaetae. Example – earthworm	Molluscs – soft body with a shell, live in water and on land.  Example – snail	Echinoderms – star shaped body, tough skin, spines, live in water.  Example – starfish
Insects – body divided into three sections, three pairs of jointed legs, antennae, two pairs of wings, body covered by a hard case. Example – housefly	Arachnids – body divided into two sections, four pairs of jointed legs, antennae, body covered by a hard case.  Example – spider	Myriapods – body divided into lots of sections, very many pairs of jointed legs, antennae, body covered by a hard case.  Example – centipede and millipede

QUESTIONS

1 Into which group (vertebrate or invertebrate) would you classify the following species?
  a fish; **b** beetle; **c** zebra; **d** crab.

2 Into which group of vertebrates would you classify the following species?
  a human; **b** snake; **c** frog; **d** trout.

3 Into which group of invertebrates would you classify the following species?
  a starfish; **b** wasp; **c** scorpion; **d** butterfly.

E Acids and alkalis

E1 ## WHAT ARE ACIDS AND ALKALIS?

TOPIC CHECKLIST

- What are acids and alkalis?
- Where do we find acids and alkalis?
- How do we know if acids and alkalis are dangerous?
- Working safely with acids and alkalis

What are acids and alkalis?

Acids and **alkalis** are two groups of chemicals. They are very important groups, as they crop up time and time again.

To explain what acids and alkalis are, we have to think about what they do. Acids are substances that react with alkalis and sometimes have a sour or sharp taste. Strong acids can eat away or **corrode** metals.

Many people think that acids are dreadful substances that will burn you if you get too close to them. Some acids do, but most acids are not **hazardous**, and many are very important to our diet, health and cleanliness.

Many everyday substances are acidic

Alkalis are substances that react with and 'cancel out' acids. Many alkalis are useful substances. Just as people often think acids are dangerous, so they think that, because alkalis are the opposite of acids, they are not dangerous. This is completely wrong. Many strong alkalis can burn living tissue and are described as **caustic**.

Where do we find acids and alkalis?

You can find lots of acids and alkalis just by looking round your house. An easy place to start is in the kitchen, because most foods are either acidic (*like an acid*) or alkaline (*like an alkali*).

Another good place to look is in the bathroom, because soaps, shampoos and other bathroom products are usually acids or alkalis.

A place that is harder to look is in your own body! Many of the substances in your body are acidic or alkaline – for example your stomach contains acid which helps to digest your food and kills some bacteria.

Some alkalis are quite hazardous, some are not

How do we know if acids and alkalis are dangerous?

Many of the acids and alkalis we have around the house are perfectly safe. How do we know which the dangerous ones are? There is a system of Hazard **Symbols**, which are put on the packaging or container of harmful substances. These are usually strong acids and alkalis.

The symbols mean the same thing whether they appear on bottles around your home, on lorries carrying acids or alkalis or in your school lab.

ⓐ A bottle of bleach has an irritant hazard sign, a bottle of drain unblocker has a corrosive sign. Which is the most dangerous?

ⓑ Vinegar and lemons are both acidic. Why don't they carry hazard symbols?

Hazard symbols	Definitions
✗ HARMFUL **Harmful**	Can make you ill if swallowed, breathed in or absorbed through the skin
✗ IRRITANT **Irritant**	May cause reddening or blistering of the skin
CORROSIVE **Corrosive**	Attacks and destroys living tissue, including eyes and skin

Working safely with acids and alkalis

Always treat an unknown or unfamiliar chemical with respect, but if you see a hazard warning symbol, handle the acid or alkali with extra care. Be careful not to get it on your skin. If you do, the best thing to do is to wash it immediately with water. Water dilutes the acid or alkali (just as it dilutes orange squash) and makes it less harmful.

ⓒ Look at the picture of a hazard warning from a carton of dishwasher powder. What should you avoid when handling a strong alkali like this?

ⓓ Why should you give a drink of water to someone who has swallowed some of the powder?

läkare. VID FÖRTARING, DRICK VATTEN ELLER MJÖLK, kontakta genast läkare och visa denna förpackning eller etiketten. FRAMKALLA EJ KRÄKNING. Innehåller: Natriumdisilikat 10-30%. Importör: Procter & Gamble, Stockholm, Sverige. 020 - 35 00 29.

(UK)(IRL) KEEP OUT OF REACH OF CHILDREN. Close dispenser immediately after dosing. Irritating to eyes. Avoid contact with eyes. In case of contact with eyes, rinse immediately with plenty of water and seek medical advice. IF SWALLOWED, DRINK WATER, seek medical advice immediately and show this label or container. DO NOT INDUCE VOMITING. Procter & Gamble UK, PO Box 1EL Newcastle upon Tyne, NE99 1EL. Republic of Ireland contact: PO Box 596, Dublin 14 For further information, freephone, (UK) 0800 3285901 (IRL)1800 535640

REIZEND/IRRITANTE IRRITEREND IRRITERANDE/IRRITANT

QUESTIONS

1 List three safe acids shown on these pages.

2 List three safe alkalis shown on these pages.

3 Look at the hazard symbol for 'corrosive' substances. Explain how each part of the symbol gives the warning message.

HOW CAN WE IDENTIFY ACIDS AND ALKALIS?

Do acids and alkalis look different?

Many acids that you will meet in school are colourless liquids. So are many alkalis. Some acids and alkalis can be white crystals or powders, and some are gases. This means that you can't *look* at a substance and tell whether it as acidic or alkaline.

Using an indicator

We can tell whether a colourless liquid is an acid or alkali by adding a substance called an **indicator**. This turns a different colour depending on whether the liquid is an acid or an alkali and so shows (or indicates) which it is.

Crushing

Where do indicators come from?

They grow on trees! Well, plants mainly. Many indicators are extracted from plant materials: leaves and petals in particular. To be useful, you need a substance that is one colour when it is in an acid and a very different colour when it is in an alkali – many plant extracts just go a shade of sludgy green in both!

To make a simple indicator, crush up some leaves with some sand and water and then filter off the juice. Test the juice (the 'extract') by putting a few drops into a liquid that you know is an acid to see what colour it turns, and do the same with an alkali. If the colours are noticeably different, you have made an indicator.

Filtering

If you would like to try this out, red cabbage, raw beetroot and blackcurrants all work well.

ⓐ What colour does red cabbage turn in acids?

ⓑ What colour does beetroot turn in alkalis?

ⓒ How would you decide which is an acid and which an alkali using blackcurrants?

	Red cabbage	Beetroot	Blackcurrant
In acid			
In alkali			

Common indicators

Until recently, the most commonly used indicator in schools was litmus, which is a dye extracted from a **lichen** that can be used as a liquid or soaked into strips of filter paper to make litmus paper. Many schools now use **Universal Indicator**, also called **pH paper**. This is made by mixing together many different indicators, most of which are made from plants.

As well as litmus and Universal Indicator, you may come across others such as phenolphthalein and methyl orange.

Indicator	Litmus solution	Universal Indicator	Phenolphthalein	Methyl orange
Colour in acid				
Colour in alkali				

Common acids and alkalis

The list below shows some of the acids and alkalis that are often used in schools. The list is NOT a list of all acids and alkalis – there are plenty of others.

Acids	Alkalis
hydrochloric acid	ammonium hydroxide (ammonia solution)
sulphuric acid	sodium hydroxide (caustic soda)
nitric acid	calcium hydroxide (limewater)
citric acid	potassium hydroxide (caustic potash)

d Make a table to show what colour each of the acids and alkalis named above will turn litmus solution.

QUESTIONS

1 How can you tell if a colourless liquid is an acid or an alkali?

2 Where can you get the starting materials for indicators?

3 What colour would litmus paper turn in hydrochloric acid?

4 Describe what you would see if you had a beaker containing sodium hydroxide solution and added phenolphthalein to it.

E3 HOW STRONG ARE ACIDS AND ALKALIS?

TOPIC CHECKLIST

- Measuring the strength of acids and alkalis
- What is the pH scale?
- What does 'neutral' mean?
- Strength of acids and alkalis

Measuring the strength of acids and alkalis – the pH test

Acids and alkalis have different strengths. Some acids, like sulphuric acid, can be very strong. Others, like cows' milk, are very weak acids. Strong acids or alkalis will react much more quickly than weak acids and alkalis, so they are more likely to be hazardous. This means that you should take extra care when handling strong acids and alkalis, which might mean wearing gloves and an apron or laboratory coat as well as the goggles you would normally use.

To find out how strong acids are we use Universal Indicator, either as paper (often called pH paper) or as a solution called U.I. (for Universal Indicator) solution. When an acid or an alkali is tested with Universal Indicator, the colour of the indicator changes. Unlike litmus, the indicator turns different colours depending on how strong or weak the acid or alkali is.

If you don't want to get any of the coloured dyes from the indicator into the acid or alkali you are testing you can use a glass rod to put a drop of the solution onto pH paper.

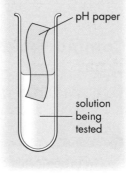

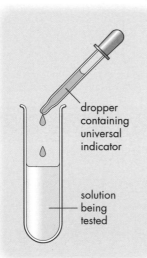

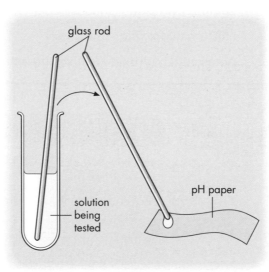

a Which method above would you use if you only had pH paper and you didn't want to change the colour of the solution you were testing?

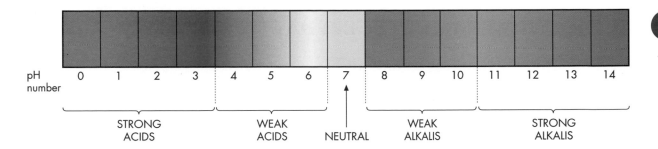

pH number	0	1	2	3	4	5	6	7	8	9	10	11	12	13	14

STRONG ACIDS   WEAK ACIDS   NEUTRAL   WEAK ALKALIS   STRONG ALKALIS

What is the pH scale?

The **pH scale** shows the range of strengths of acids and alkalis. On this scale, the strongest acid is 0 and the strongest alkali is 14. Universal Indicator turns a different colour for all the numbers (**pH values**) on the pH scale. You can find out whether a substance is an acid or alkali and how strong it is by testing it with Universal Indicator solution or pH paper and then comparing the colour to this chart.

a

b

b For each of the photographs on the right, write down the letter of the photograph, the pH number and the strength (strong or weak) of each acid or alkali.

What does 'neutral' mean?

Things that aren't acids *and* aren't alkalis are **neutral**. Any solution that has a pH number of 7 is neutral. Pure water has a pH of 7.

c

d

c What colour would Universal Indicator solution or pH paper turn in pure water?

Strength of acids and alkalis

Look again at the pH scale. You will see that numbers under 7 are acids, and numbers over 7 are alkalis. For numbers under 7 the lower the number is, the stronger the acid is, but for numbers over 7, the higher the number the stronger the alkali is.

QUESTIONS

1 What does Universal Indicator tell you about an acid or alkali that litmus doesn't?

2 Universal Indicator turns dark green when it is added to a solution. What does this tell you about the solution?

3 In the lab you find two bottles, each containing a colourless solution. There is a hazard warning label for 'corrosive' lying next to them. When the two solutions are tested, solution A is pH 2 and solution B is pH 8. Which bottle is the 'corrosive' label probably from?

4 In question 3, should you stick the corrosive label back on the bottle? Explain your answer.

5 Why do you need to take extra safety precautions when using strong acids or alkalis?

ACIDS AND ALKALIS IN EVERYDAY SITUATIONS

How are acids and alkalis useful?

Millions of tonnes of acids and alkalis are used every year to make chemicals such as fertilizers, soaps, plastics, paints and drugs. We meet acids and alkalis in our everyday lives when we wash our skin or hair, treat insect stings or cure indigestion.

Food preservation

Food can be preserved in a variety of ways, but the one that involves acids is called 'pickling'. This involves soaking the food in vinegar, which is acidic enough that it kills the bacteria which cause the food to decay.

Pickled walnuts

Hair and skin care

To keep our skin in the best condition possible, it should be slightly acidic. This does not mean that you should jump into a bath of strong acid used for cleaning metals! The best pH value for skin has been measured at pH5.5 - between pH5 and pH6. That's why you may have seen skin care products with pH5.5 on the label.

Plant and insect stings

When ants and nettles bite or sting you they release formic acid under your skin. This hurts – your body doesn't like to be injected with acid! Bee stings are also acidic. All these can be treated with calamine lotion or a bicarbonate of soda solution which both cancel out the acid.

Wasp stings are alkaline. You can treat a wasp sting by putting vinegar, which is an acid, on it.

Bulldog ant

Nettle

Soil treatment

If soil has too much acid to let the crops grow properly, a farmer can add 'lime' to the soil. **Lime** is really an alkali called calcium oxide, which reacts with the acid so that there is less in the soil, and the crops can grow properly. If there is too much alkali in the soil, farmers will often spread animal manure on the field to lower the pH by cancelling out some or all of the alkali.

ⓐ Do you think animal manure is acidic or alkaline?

What happens when an acid is added to an alkali?

Acids and alkalis can 'cancel' each other out. What does this mean?

When an acid and an alkali are mixed together in the right quantities they make a neutral solution.

ACID + ALKALI = NEUTRAL

Whenever an acid (or alkali) is made neutral by adding the right amount of alkali (or acid) we can say that it has been **neutralised**, so the process of adding acid to alkali (or the other way round) to make a neutral solution is called **neutralisation**.

An alkaline substance has a pH number higher than 7. If you add an acid to it, the pH number will get lower. If you add exactly the right amount of acid, the pH number will be 7.

An acidic substance will start off with a pH number lower than 7. If you add an alkali to it, the pH number will get higher. If you add exactly the right amount of alkali, the pH number will be 7.

ⓑ What would happen to the pH if you added vinegar to a bee sting?

ⓒ Which has the higher pH number, an acid or an alkali?

QUESTIONS

1 Make a list of some uses of acids and alkalis.

2 What would you add to an acid to raise the pH?

3 To neutralise an alkali, do you need to raise or lower the pH?

4 Give two examples to show how neutralisation can be useful to us.

5 Explain why bee stings and wasp stings are treated differently.

WHAT HAPPENS WHEN ACIDS REACT WITH ALKALIS?

TOPIC CHECKLIST

- When is stomach acid a problem?
- Which is the best cure?

When is stomach acid a problem?

A common cause of stomach ache is 'acid indigestion'.
This means that your digestion isn't working properly because
there's too much acid in your stomach. Your stomach needs
acid to help break down **proteins** and sugars in your food but
too much is painful.

ⓐ What can you add to an acid to neutralise it?

What can you do about acid indigestion? There are plenty of
indigestion remedies in the shops. The photograph on the right
shows just some of the vast range that is available. All of these
indigestion remedies are designed to reduce the amount of
excess (extra) acid so that the stomach stops sending pain
messages to your brain.

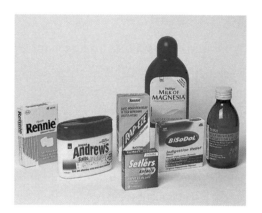

These remedies contain chemicals called **antacids**. An antacid is
any substance that will use up an acid. This includes alkalis
which neutralise the acid.

When you buy an indigestion remedy you often get a powder
that dissolves to make a weak alkali. You shouldn't take too
much of this solution, because your stomach won't work
properly unless it is quite acidic. This raises the question 'how
much acid does an antacid use up?'

**ⓑ Do you think that one dose of any antacid will always
cancel out the same amount of acid?**

Which is the best cure?

To find the answer to this question we must first decide what
we mean by 'best cure'. Does this mean the tablet that uses up
the most acid, or the one that uses up acid the quickest, or the
one that is the cheapest? To find out, we must carry out one or
more investigations.

If we are going to test antacids to find out which one uses up the
most acid, we will need a way to tell when all the acid is used up.

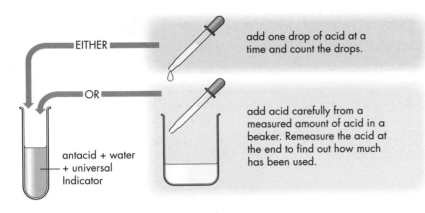

EITHER — add one drop of acid at a time and count the drops.

OR — add acid carefully from a measured amount of acid in a beaker. Remeasure the acid at the end to find out how much has been used.

antacid + water + universal Indicator

One way to do this is to mix one recommended dose of the antacid with water and a few drops of Universal Indicator solution, then add acid a little at a time until the indicator turns a colour that shows that the solution is neutral.

The amount of acid used up can be worked out either by adding acid one drop at a time and counting the drops, or by measuring (in a measuring cylinder) the amount of acid at the start and subtracting the amount of acid left at the end.

c **What colours would show that the acid hasn't all been used up?**

d **Why isn't this a very fair comparison of different antacids?**

To find out which remedy is the cheapest, you could find out how much acid was neutralised by one dose of antacid and then divide the answer by the cost of one dose in pence. This would tell you the amount of acid that would be neutralised by one pennyworth of antacid.

$$\text{amount of acid neutralised per penny} = \frac{\text{amount of acid used up by one dose}}{\text{cost of one dose in pence}}$$

one dose = one dose of antacid

e **Is this a fair comparison of different antacids? Explain your answer.**

QUESTIONS

1 What is an antacid?

2 Which of the investigations above would give the 'fairest' comparison? Explain your answer.

3 Should you use up all the acid in the stomach to cure a stomach ache? Explain your answer.

F1 WHAT IS A CHEMICAL REACTION?

> **TOPIC CHECKLIST**
> - What is a chemical change?
> - Looking at chemical reactions

What is a chemical change?

There are changes all around us, for example lakes freeze in winter, sugar dissolves in a cup of tea, water evaporates from a lake, and coal burns in a fire. Some changes are what scientists call **chemical changes**, and some are not.

How can we tell the difference?

As you will see, there are different ways to spot a chemical change, but there is only one thing that MUST happen during every chemical change. A chemical change takes place when new substances are made that are different from the substances that we started with. Any new substance produced during a chemical change is called a **product** of the change. The substances we start with are called **reactants**.

One way to work out if the products are really new or not is to ask yourself the question 'can I get the starting materials back again?' If you can, then nothing new has been made. For example, water turns to ice when it freezes but ice is just solid water, so when it gets warmer again the ice turns back to water – you are back to the starting materials.

ⓐ **Not all changes are chemical changes. Can you spot the one chemical change in the photographs above?**

Looking at chemical reactions

Whenever a chemical change takes place, there must have been a chemical reaction.

Many chemical reactions happen when two or more substances are added together. If any of the following happen when you do this you know that a chemical reaction is taking place.

Does it fizz?

If you see bubbling, a gas is being 'given off' or 'released'. This means that a new substance (the gas) is being made, so it is a chemical reaction. For example, when **bicarbonate of soda** is put into lemon juice, the mixture fizzes as carbon dioxide gas is released.

When bicarbonate of soda is put into lemon juice a gas is released

Does it smell?

If you smell a new smell during a change, this means that a gas has been released even though you didn't see any bubbles, which means that a chemical reaction has probably taken place.

Do the products look different?

When a chemical reaction takes place, the products often, but not always, look different to the reactants. They may be a different colour. For example, if you put a piece of magnesium into some blue copper II sulphate solution, the blue colour disappears as the copper sulphate and magnesium change into new products. The products can often look just the same as the reactants.

Does it get hot or cold?

If the reaction gets either hot or cold without *you* heating or cooling it, a chemical change has taken place. For example, explosions are the result of very fast and violent chemical reactions that release a lot of heat as well as light.

b Describe three observations that would tell you that new products had been made.

c Why is it not always a good idea to measure a change in temperature with your hand?

QUESTIONS

1 What is the one thing that always happens in a chemical reaction?

a — a smelly change
b — a bubbling change
c — a melting change
d — a change that gets hot

2 Which of the changes in the diagram above are chemical reactions, and which are not chemical reactions?

3 Why is it a sign of a chemical reaction if gas is given off?

HOW DO ACIDS REACT WITH METALS?

Acids and corrosion

Some acids are **corrosive**. This means that they will eat away or **corrode** other substances. The photograph shows an iron tray, that a car battery sits on, after it was corroded by acid escaping from the battery.

When acids corrode substances, what is really happening is a chemical reaction. The acids react to form new substances. When the iron in the picture corrodes one new substance is a powder, which washes away. The other is a gas called **hydrogen**, which floats away. This is why holes are left behind.

When acids react with metals hydrogen gas is usually produced because of the hydrogen that is present in most acids: when acids react the hydrogen is released.

A test for hydrogen gas

How do we know that hydrogen is released? You usually see bubbles in the reaction, but these could be any invisible gas. Hydrogen gas has no colour, no particular smell and no taste, so how can we prove that it is there?

Luckily, hydrogen has some unusual properties that make it possible to identify it. First, it is much lighter than air – a balloon filled with hydrogen rises very quickly – and secondly hydrogen burns easily and quickly. We can use these properties to collect hydrogen and to test it.

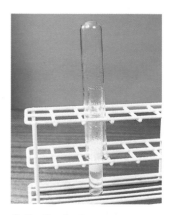

Collecting hydrogen gas

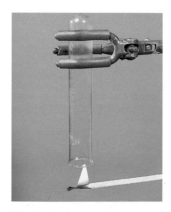

Testing hydrogen gas

Simple chemical reactions

If hydrogen is released during a reaction, it will rise, and this means that we can catch the hydrogen by putting a container over the reaction.

If we collect the hydrogen gas in a test tube and then set fire to it by putting a burning splint at the end of the tube, the hydrogen burns with a squeaky 'pop' sound. Because hydrogen is the only common gas that does this, we say that this test *proves* that hydrogen has been produced.

Acids reacting with metals

Some metals react with acids more enthusiastically than others. You can tell how readily a metal reacts with acid by the number of bubbles given off in a certain time. When you compare different metals reacting with the same acid you can see at once which is producing the most bubbles.

Calcium   Magnesium   Zinc   Iron

The pictures above show what you see just after an acid is added to four different metals.

ⓐ which metal is reacting most with the acid?

ⓑ which metal is reacting least with the acid?

If you can collect enough gas to test with a burning splint, you will always find that the gas released by a metal reacting with an acid burns with a squeaky pop, showing that the gas is hydrogen.

QUESTIONS

1 What gas is released when most metals react with acid?

2 Is hydrogen gas lighter than air or heavier than air?

3 If they were put into the same acid, which of iron and magnesium would produce more hydrogen gas in one minute?

HOW DO ACIDS REACT WITH CARBONATES?

TOPIC CHECKLIST

- Carbon dioxide
- A test for carbon dioxide
- What is a carbonate?
- Acids reacting with carbonates

Carbon dioxide

Hydrogen is not the only colourless, odourless (no smell) and tasteless gas that can be given off during reactions involving acids. When acids react with chemicals called carbonates they release carbon dioxide.

Carbon dioxide is as difficult to detect as hydrogen but that is where the similarity ends. Carbon dioxide is heavier than air and does not burn at all – carbon dioxide is used in fire extinguishers to put fires out. You come across carbon dioxide quite often in everyday life – it's the gas that gives fizzy drinks their fizz, and one of the gases that you breathe out.

A test for carbon dioxide

To see whether a gas released in a reaction is carbon dioxide we have to bubble it through calcium hydroxide solution. This is often called **limewater**, though it has nothing to do with the fruit called lime. If it is carbon dioxide the limewater turns a misty white colour so that it looks like thin watery milk.

There are lots different ways of getting the carbon dioxide into the limewater. For example:

A you can suck the gas out of the reaction vessel with a dropper and squeeze it into a test tube containing a little limewater;

B you can pour the gas out of the reaction vessel into a test tube containing a little limewater;

C you can connect a delivery tube and bung to the reaction vessel and bubble the gas directly through the limewater.

Carbon dioxide gas is the only gas that can make limewater turn milky.

ⓐ **Why can you pour invisible carbon dioxide out of the reaction vessel and expect the gas to go into the limewater tube?**

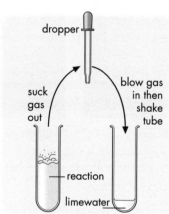

A: moving the gas with a dropper

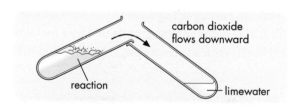

B: pouring the gas

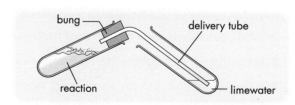

C: using a delivery tube

What is a carbonate?

Chalk rock
(calcium carbonate)

Marble
(calcium carbonate)

Baking powder
(sodium hydrogen
carbonate)

Indigestion remedy
(sodium hydrogen
carbonate)

Carbonates are a group of chemicals which all contain carbon and oxygen, which is released as carbon dioxide gas when they react with acids.

Carbonates are all around you. All the things in the pictures above contain carbonates.

Acids reacting with carbonates

In the photographs below you can see different acids reacting with some different carbonates. As these pictures suggest, most carbonates react very well with most acids, and release carbon dioxide gas during the reaction.

Dilute hydrochloric acid
reacting with calcium
carbonate powder

Dilute nitric acid reacting
with crushed limestone

Dilute sulphuric acid
reacting with sodium
carbonate crystals

b How can you tell a chemical reaction is taking place?

QUESTIONS

1 Give three similarities between hydrogen and carbon dioxide.

2 Give two differences between them

3 How do you test for carbon dioxide?

4 Limewater is a clear solution. When you bubble carbon dioxide through limewater, the limewater turns milky. If you keep bubbling carbon dioxide through the same limewater it turns clear again and then won't change again. What sort of change is happening in the limewater?

WHAT HAPPENS DURING BURNING?

Is burning a chemical reaction?

Yes it is. How can we be sure though? If you look back to Topic F1 – 'What is a chemical reaction' – you can remind yourself (if necessary) of the signs that tell us that a chemical change has taken place.

ⓐ What tells us that a chemical change is taking place when paper burns?

ⓑ What tells us that a chemical change is taking place when methane gas burns, for example in a gas cooker?

Burning needs oxygen

What is **oxygen**? Oxygen is yet another colourless, odourless, tasteless gas, but it has very different properties to hydrogen and carbon dioxide. Oxygen helps things to burn, so the test for oxygen is to light a wooden splint, blow the splint out and put the glowing end of the splint into the gas. If the gas is mostly oxygen, the splint will rekindle (or relight)!

Oxygen is the gas in the air that substances react with when they burn.

Burning is a chemical reaction between a **fuel** and oxygen. The reaction usually needs heat to start it off and to keep it going.

The **fire triangle** may help you to remember the three things needed for a fire: take one away and the fire will go out.

What is made during burning?

As burning is a chemical reaction, one or more new substances *must* be made when something burns. Burning substances in air and oxygen usually gives the same product, but there is not very much oxygen in air compared with pure oxygen, so substances burn better in oxygen than in air.

What do we mean by better? They burn faster and with a brighter, hotter flame.

Paper burning

Methane burning

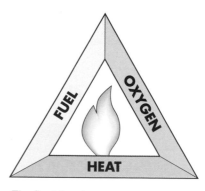

The fire triangle

This means you have to be very careful when burning things in oxygen – the results can be startling as many substances that burn in air with a small flame can flare up in pure oxygen. Because things burn so well in oxygen there is a danger of things getting out of hand, and the fire spreading to other **combustible** ('burnable') materials nearby – including your fingers!

There is also the risk that if you burn something in a glass container the extreme heat can cause the glass to crack or shatter.

What is made when substances burn in oxygen?

Whenever a substance burns in oxygen, an **oxide** will be made. Some are called oxides, and some are called dioxides.

For example, if we burn magnesium in oxygen, magnesium joins with oxygen to make magnesium oxide. We can write this in a chemical shorthand called a 'word equation':

magnesium + oxygen → magnesium oxide

here, the '+' means 'joins with' and the arrow means 'to make'

If we burn sulphur in oxygen, sulphur dioxide is made.

sulphur + oxygen → sulphur dioxide

C Write a sentence which gives the same information as the word equation for sulphur burning in oxygen.

Magnesium burning in air

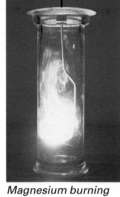
Magnesium burning in oxygen

Sulphur burning in air

Sulphur burning in oxygen

QUESTIONS

1 Which gas in the air is needed for burning?

2 Use the fire triangle to explain why a fire goes out when you pour cold water on it.

3 Use the fire triangle to explain what happens to a fire when you cover it with a fire blanket.

4 Write the word equation for the reaction that takes place when we burn:

   a) calcium in oxygen

   b) iron in oxygen

   c) zinc in oxygen

   d) carbon in oxygen

5 Design a fire safety leaflet or poster to explain the extra hazards to guard against when burning substances in pure oxygen in the laboratory, and what precautions should be taken to reduce the risks as far as possible.

WHAT'S IN A FUEL?

TOPIC CHECKLIST

- What are fuels?
- What are fossil fuels?
- Burning natural gas

What are fuels?

Fuels are substances that burn to release heat energy that we can use. Anything that doesn't burn can't be a fuel, even if it is an **energy source**.

ⓐ Draw a table with three columns headed solid fuels, liquid fuels and gas fuels. Put the substances from the photos on this page into the correct column.

ⓑ Which *one* of the substances from the photos on this page is not a fuel? Why not?

Camping gas   Petrol   Electric fire   Bonfire   Jet fuel

What are fossil fuels?

Fossil fuels are naturally occurring fuels that have been formed in a similar way to fossils - they have been squeezed and heated underground for a very long time. There are three main fossil fuels, which are coal, oil and natural gas. These are all rich in carbon.

ⓒ What gas will be made when carbon burns in oxygen?

Simple chemical reactions

Burning natural gas

The natural gas which burns in our cookers is usually at least 95% methane gas. Methane gas is made of hydrogen and carbon.

When carbon joins with oxygen during burning it makes carbon dioxide. When hydrogen joins with oxygen it makes water. So carbon dioxide and water vapour will be produced when methane burns in a good supply of air. We can show this as a word equation:

$$methane + oxygen \rightarrow carbon\ dioxide + water\ vapour$$

The heat is not mentioned in the word equation because heat is a form of energy, and is not a substance.

d **What kind of change has taken place?**

The experiment in the diagram below shows you how we can collect and detect the gases produced when methane burns.

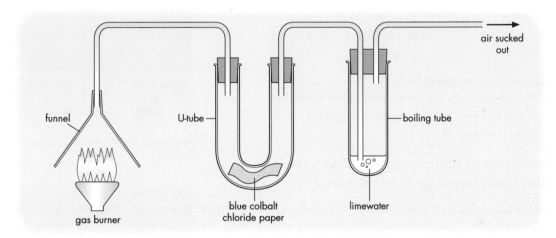

Air is sucked through the apparatus by a pump. This pulls the gases from the flame into the funnel and through the U-tube and boiling tube. Blue cobalt chloride paper turns pink when there is water vapour in the air so when the cobalt chloride paper turns pink you know that the burning gas has made water vapour. The limewater in the boiling tube turns milky as the gases from the flame bubble through it.

e **Which gas has turned the limewater milky?**

f **What are the two gases made by the burning methane gas?**

QUESTIONS

1 What is a fuel?

2 What are the three main fossil fuels?

3 What gas do fuels react with when they burn?

4 What gas is always produced when a fossil fuel burns in plenty of air?

5 Paraffin has carbon and hydrogen in it. What two gases will it produce when it burns?

Air and burning

How do we know that burning just uses part of the air and not all of the gases in the air? Here is one experiment that is often used to show this.

Put a large glass container over a burning candle floating on (or standing in) a trough of water. The burning candle uses up part of the air in the glass jar. This means that there is less air in the jar and the water rises up to fill the space. When the candle goes out you can measure how far the water has risen and this is the amount of air used up by the candle burning.

By measuring the change in water level, you can work out the percentage of the air used up. We know from other work that this part of the air is oxygen, because that's the gas that reacts with substances that are burning.

A burning candle uses up oxygen

ⓐ If the glass container is 50 cm high and the water rises 10cm, what percentage of the air has been used up?

ⓑ What percentage of the air is oxygen?

ⓒ If you did the same experiment with a different sized jar and candle, what percentage of the air would you expect to be used up?

What happens to the products?

The calculation above is neat and tidy, but it ignores an important fact: *every chemical reaction produces new substances.*

In this case, the burning wax produces carbon dioxide gas and water vapour, and scientists have worked out that more carbon dioxide and water vapour are made than the amount of oxygen used up. So why isn't the water pushed down as it should be?

Something must have happened to the carbon dioxide and water vapour, otherwise the water level could not possibly rise.

The water level rises

ⓓ Where *could* the water vapour have gone?

ⓔ Where *could* the carbon dioxide have gone?

How long will a candle burn for?

When does the candle in the gas jar go out? The answer is 'when there is no more oxygen left to let the wax keep burning'.

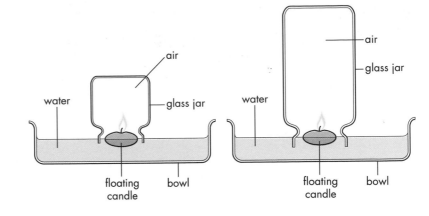

f If air always has the same percentage of oxygen in it, will the same sized candle burn for less time, more time or the same time in a larger container? Explain your answer.

By answering this question, you have written a prediction.

One way to test your prediction would be to burn a candle in different sized containers of air and time how long it stays alight.

Each container would have to hold a different volume of air, but all the containers should allow the use of the same sized candle. The length of time the candles burn should be timed exactly.

Here is a table of results from an experiment like this.

g Draw a graph with the volume of the container on the bottom axis and the time the candle stays alight for on the side axis.

If most of the points on your graph show a trend upwards as the container gets bigger, it shows that the more air there is the longer the candle burns.

h What does the graph from question (g) show?

i If some of the points on your graph are well away from the pattern shown by the rest of the points, what do you think you should do?

Volume of container (cm³)	Time that the candle stays alight (seconds)
100	5
200	10
300	15
400	17
500	20
600	25

QUESTIONS

1 Write down a plan for an investigation to find out how long a candle burns in different amounts of air. Explain clearly *what* you will do (and *why* you will do it) to make sure that it is a fair test.

HOW ARE THEORIES CREATED?

TOPIC CHECKLIST

- A bright idea?
- What are solids, liquids and gases?

A bright idea?

Two and a half thousand years ago, Greek **philosophers** (thinkers) tried to decide what things were made of. Parmenides had the idea (or **theory**) that everything in the universe was made up of one kind of 'stuff'. Empedocles developed this theory, saying that everything was actually made up of one or a combination of four **elements** – earth, air, fire and water.

Leusippus decided that this wasn't sensible and argued that everything was made up of tiny particles, called **atoms**, which could not be destroyed. Democritus was a follower of Leusippus and developed this theory further, stating that there must be lots of different kinds of atoms, but all of them were tiny, round objects that couldn't change size or shape.

Some years later, a famous philosopher called Aristotle collected together and wrote down what he thought were the best theories of the time. The theory that Aristotle decided was the best explanation of 'what things are made of', was the theory of everything being made from four elements: earth, air, fire and water.

The Greek philosophers believed in the power of reason to understand how things worked.

Aristotle's views survived because his book survived when others, including Democritus' books, were lost. For the next 2000 years it was Aristotle's chosen theory that people read and believed.

It was only in the 17th century that scientists started to question Aristotle's theory because it did not fit with the way things actually behaved. A man called John Dalton did many experiments to try to work out what things were made of. When he looked at what he had found out (his **evidence**) he decided on the same theory as Democritus to explain it. He argued that everything is made of tiny **particles**.

ⓐ What name did Leusippus give to his 'tiny particle'?

ⓑ What did John Dalton do to help him decide which was the best idea?

ⓒ How were Empedocles' ideas different from those of Parmenides?

What are solids, liquids and gases?

You probably know that solids keep the same shape and size, liquids keep the same size but can change their shape, and gases can change their shape and size and spread out to fill whatever container they are in.

(d) For each of the following substances, decide whether it is a solid, a liquid or a gas. Write a sentence about each one. You can start: 'xxxxx is a solid because ...'

A rock

Sea water

Helium-filled balloons

A sandcastle

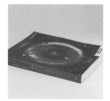

A book

A fizzy drink

Solids keep the same size and shape.

Liquids stay the same size, but not the same shape.

Gases change size and shape.

QUESTIONS

1. A block of iron and a block of aluminium of exactly the same size have different masses. Is there anything in Democritus' theory that might explain this?

2. Look at the information below. Write down any theory that explains all the information.
   - Solids and liquids are made of particles.
   - Solids don't change their shape.
   - Liquids can change their shape.

3. Now look at this piece of information: 'Solids can turn into liquids when they are heated.' Does your theory in question 1 still work now you have this extra information, or do you need to change to a new theory that explains all the information?

HOW DO SOLIDS, LIQUIDS AND GASES BEHAVE?

TOPIC CHECKLIST

- Why do solids, liquids and gases behave like this?
- Can particles explain what we see?

Why do solids liquids and gases behave like this?

What makes solids, liquids and gases behave differently? This is just the sort of question that scientists from very early times asked themselves. We will look at what scientists think today, later in the unit.

But for now, put yourself in the place of a scientist. Look at the evidence here of the way solids, liquids and gases behave and see if you can come up with any theories about the reason for this. Work with a friend or in groups if it helps.

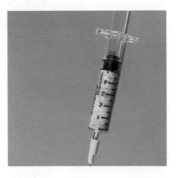

When you try to squash a syringe full of a solid, you can't.

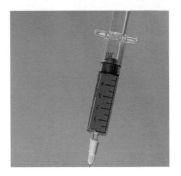

When you try to squash a syringe full of a liquid, you can't.

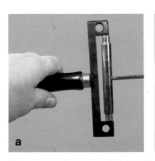  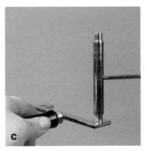

When you heat a solid, it will usually get bigger, or expand. When the bar in the photograph (a) is heated it gets longer (b) and thicker (c).

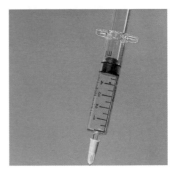

When you try to squash a syringe full of a gas, you can.

When you put a coloured crystal into water, the crystal dissolves and the colour spreads out. The hotter the water, the quicker the colour spreads out.

When you heat the end of this rod, the paperclips fall off in order (they are stuck on with wax which melts when it gets warm). The one nearest the flame falls off first, then the next nearest and so on.

When you hang masses on the end of a wire, the wire will stretch and stretch and then eventually snap.

Can particles explain what we see?

Does the idea that everything is made of tiny particles arranged in different ways explain how solids, liquids and gases behave? Look at the information and answer the questions below. Remember the idea that particles are round objects that can't change size or shape.

ⓐ Fergus says that the syringes show that the particles in a solid must be closer together than the particles in a gas. Why does he say this?

Fergus

ⓑ Ravinder says that the metal bar gets bigger when it's heated because the particles get further apart; Rachel says it's because the particles are expanding. Who do you agree with, and why?

Ravinder

ⓒ Sarah says that the smell from a bottle of perfume spreads out because the gas particles flow; Harminder says it happens because gas particles can move in all directions. Who do you agree with, and why?

Sarah

ⓓ Umesh says that crystals spread out faster in hot water because they break down into particles faster, but Siobhan says it happens because the particles move around faster when they are hot. Who do you agree with, and why?

Umesh

Pip

ⓔ Pip says that the wire gets thinner because the particles are changing shape. Does this fit with Democritus' theory?

ⓕ John says that the rod and paperclips don't tell us anything about particles. Do you agree?

John

QUESTIONS

1 Write down one thing that all solids do.

2 Write down what happens to the gas in a perfume bottle when the bottle is opened.

3 Draw a table with three columns headed 'solids', 'liquids' and 'gases'. Write the names of as many solids, liquids and gases as you can into the correct column of your table.

DIFFERENCES BETWEEN SOLIDS, LIQUIDS AND GASES

> **TOPIC CHECKLIST**
>
> ● Classifying solids, liquids and gases
> ● Things that aren't solids, liquids or gases
> ● Properties of solids, liquids and gases

Classifying solids, liquids and gases

How do we decide whether a substance is a solid, a liquid or a gas? We have to look at what its **properties** are, or the way the substance behaves. You already know that solids keep the same shape and volume, liquids keep the same volume but not shape, and gases can change their shape and volume depending on where you put them.

ⓐ Construct a key to classify materials as solid, liquid, gas or mixture. Your first question could be 'Does it always keep its own shape?'

ⓑ Use your key to decide whether the substances in the photo are solids, liquids or gases.

propane   petrol   camping gas   water

marble   wood   sand   iron   jelly   ketchup

Things that aren't solids, liquids or gases

You probably found that not all the things in the photograph fit your definition of a solid, liquid or gas. For example, tomato sauce can change its shape *very slowly* but not its volume, so is it a solid or a liquid?

ⓒ Based on what you *think* now, is tomato sauce a solid that changes its shape slowly or a liquid that can't change its shape very well?

ⓓ Look at the label from a tomato sauce bottle. Make a list of the substances in tomato sauce.

ⓔ For each of the substances in (d) write down whether it is a solid or a liquid.

ⓕ Why do you think that tomato sauce sometimes behaves like a solid and sometimes like a liquid?

TOMATO KETCHUP
We are very proud of Heinz Tomato Ketchup. One of the original Heinz '57 Varieties', our ketchup has stood for quality and authenticity for over 100 years. If you are not delighted with this ketchup simply write to us quoting the quality code on the bottle cap for a full refund. Your statutory rights are not affected.
INGREDIENTS: Tomatoes (126g per 100g Ketchup), Spirit Vinegar Glucose Syrup, Sugar, Salt, Spice and Herb Extracts, Spice, Garlic Powder.

NUTRITION INFORMATION		
TYPICAL VALUES	PER 100g	PER SERVING (10ml)

Hopefully by now you have spotted the fact that this is a trick question. Tomato sauce isn't one substance; it is a mixture of lots of different substances. Mixtures behave differently to pure substances.

You will find that most of the substances which don't fit neatly into one category from solids, liquids or gases, are mixtures. For example, all **foams** are mixtures of a gas and something else.

g **Do you think the 'something else' in a foam is usually a solid or a liquid?**

A **gel** is a mixture of a solid and a liquid. This means that a gel can keep the same shape but it can be made to flow as well – you can experiment (carefully!) with hair gel at home to see this close up!

Flowing flour is another example of a mixture behaving differently. A lump made of lots of flour grains stuck together would not flow, but flour grains certainly do.

h **What is the flour mixed with?**

Gels are useful in all sorts of ways.

Properties of solids, liquids and gases

Why do they do what they do?

You have seen a lot of evidence about the way solids, liquids and gases behave and thought about whether the theory of particles can explain it.

i **Can the ideas you discussed on the previous page explain how tomato sauce or a foam behave?**

It was mentioned on previous pages that the idea of things being made up of bits has been around for a long time. Imagine you were looking down an extremely powerful microscope that would let you see the smallest bits inside any substance.

j **Draw or describe what you think you might see when you look at solids, at liquids and at gases.**

> **QUESTIONS**
>
> 1 Use your key to classify the following: iron, oxygen, **granite**, water, paper, sand, jelly, talcum powder, toothpaste, reusable adhesive, milk, cola drink.
>
> 2 By yourself or in a group, think about your answer(s) to question (i) and then decide whether your idea explains how solids, liquids and gases behave or not.

THE PARTICLE MODEL OF SOLIDS, LIQUIDS AND GASES

TOPIC CHECKLIST

- What is a particle?
- The particle theory
- Does the particle theory explain everything?

What is a particle?

A particle is a very small 'bit' of something. When we talk about particles here we are talking about 'bits' which are so small we can hardly see them even with the most powerful microscope.

They cannot be destroyed and the particles in each substance have a fixed shape and size. It is the way these particles are arranged that decides whether a substance is a solid, liquid or gas.

How can a model help?

It is very difficult to imagine how invisible particles are behaving inside a solid, liquid or gas. To help us imagine this we can use a **model**, which is like the thing we can't see, so that we can get a better idea of how it works.

To help us imagine invisible particles in solids, liquids and gases we can look at how sand behaves.

In **sandstone** the grains of sand are 'glued' in place and cannot move, so sandstone behaves just like a solid – it stays the same shape and size.

In sand the same grains are there, and are still very close to each other, but they can move. This means that sand can change its shape as the grains flow over each other, just like a liquid.

In a sandstorm the same grains of sand are being blown around in different directions at different speeds, and are spread far apart. This means that one bucketful of sand will take up a lot more space when it is part of a sandstorm, and the shape and volume of the sand change constantly – just like a smelly gas spreads everywhere in a small room!

The particle theory

The sand model we have just used is a good way to imagine the theory, or model, of particles.

In solids we think that millions of tiny particles are all fixed close together so that they are held in place. Each individual particle is only able to move about by moving or vibrating backwards, forwards, side to side, or up and down (rather like jiggling on the spot), but can't leave its place.

Sandstone

Sand

A sandstorm

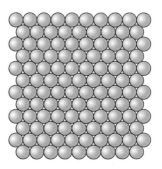

How particles are arranged in a solid

The particles in a liquid are the same particles as in a solid. The particles are still close, and can still vibrate in any direction, but in a liquid the particles are not fixed in place so as they vibrate (jiggle around) they move past each other.

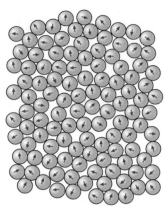

How particles are arranged in a liquid

The particles in a gas are arranged very differently to either a solid or a liquid. The particles are spread out and are moving around randomly – in any and every direction – and very quickly. The particles bash into each other and into the walls of whatever container they are put in.

ⓐ **How is this theory similar to our sand model?**

ⓑ **How is it different?**

Does the particle theory explain everything?

To see if this particle theory is of any use, we must see if it can explain the properties of solids, liquids and gases.

Answer these questions about the particle model, but always explain your answer:

Look at the particle model for a solid.

ⓒ **Does the model explain why a solid stays the same size?**

ⓓ **Does the model explain why a solid stays the same shape?**

Look at the particle model for a liquid.

ⓔ **Does the model explain why a liquid stays the same size?**

ⓕ **Does the model explain why a liquid can change shape?**

Look at the particle model for a gas.

ⓖ **Does the model explain why a gas doesn't stay the same size?**

ⓗ **Does the model explain why a gas doesn't stay the same shape?**

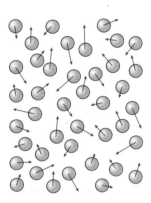

How particles are arranged in a gas

QUESTIONS

1 Write down one difference between the particle model for a solid and the particle model for a liquid.

2 Write down one difference between the particle model for a liquid and the particle model for a gas.

3 For each of your answers to questions 1 and 2, explain how the difference in the arrangement of particles affects the way solids, liquids and gases behave.

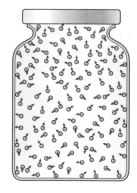

- How can it explain gas pressure?
- How can it explain diffusion?

If the particle theory is any good it should do more than just explain the easy bits. Can the particle theory explain more complex observations?

How can it explain gas pressure?

Any gas pushes against the walls of whatever container it is put in. The gas particles exert a **pressure** because they are hitting all the walls all the time. The more gas particles hit the wall each second, the higher the pressure.

Air is just a mixture of gases, so particles hitting things explains why air has a pressure.

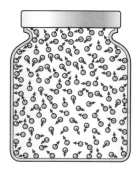

(a) **The two containers in the pictures have the same amount of the same gas in them. Why do the gas particles in the small container hit the walls more often than the ones in the large container?**

Investigating gas pressure

Most 'empty cans' aren't empty at all, they're full of air. If you remove all the air from inside the can, the can collapses. Can the particle theory explain why?

When this was first done, people thought that the can was being sucked inwards, but when we think about the particles involved we can see that really the can is being squashed by the particles pushing from the outside, because there are no particles inside to resist their pressure.

Actually, there are usually a few million particles left inside the can, so it is really a case of the large number of particles outside the can pushing harder than the small number of particles inside the can, so the can collapses.

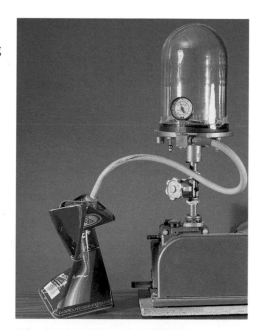

Why does an empty can collapse?

More gas effects

If you stand in a room with a ray of sunshine coming through the window at the right angle, you can often see tiny specks (or **motes**) of dust that seem to dance in the air, even when there isn't a draught.

ⓑ What could be hitting the dust motes to make them move?

How can it explain diffusion?

When a coloured crystal is put onto **agar jelly**, the colour spreads out as particles from the crystal break away from the crystal and spread through the agar. This is caused by the movement of the crystal particles and the agar particles. This spreading out movement is called **diffusion**.

Diffusion in liquids

It is possible to make a layer of coloured ink at the bottom of a beaker of water. There is a nice sharp boundary between the two layers, so common sense says that the ink should stay just where it is.

The particle theory says something different. If the particles are moving about, which they do in liquids, then they will start to mix with the water particles, and the colour will gradually spread out.

This is what really happens, which is evidence that the particle theory is correct.

Diffusion in gases

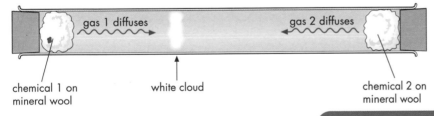

chemical 1 on mineral wool   white cloud   chemical 2 on mineral wool

In the tube above, a gas spreads out (diffuses) from each of the chemicals at the ends. When the two gases meet, a chemical reaction takes place and a white cloud is made.

ⓒ Look at the diagram. Which gas, 1 or 2, must have diffused faster?

ⓓ Explain your answer to question (c).

QUESTIONS

1 Explain why a can with very little air inside collapses.

2 Look at the particle explanation of diffusion again and then explain why you can smell perfume from an open perfume bottle held at arm's length.

3 Use the particle theory to explain each of the pieces of evidence in Topic G1, such as the syringes and the bar-and-gauge.

H Solutions

HOW CAN WE TELL WHEN A LIQUID IS A MIXTURE?

> **TOPIC CHECKLIST**
>
> - How can we tell if something is dissolved?
> - What do soluble and insoluble mean?
> - How do you separate the mixture?
> - Why can't we separate solutions by filtering?

How can we tell if something is dissolved?

Most of the time, you *can't* tell if a liquid has something dissolved in it or not. If water has salt or sugar dissolved in it you can't tell just by looking.

Sometimes a colour is left in the liquid. When you dissolve instant coffee in water the liquid is brown. In the copper sulphate solution you can see below, the liquid is a clear blue. But very often the **solution** of something dissolved in water is a clear liquid, which looks the same as water.

ⓐ **One of the beakers on the right has a poison dissolved in it, the other is pure water. Can you be certain which has the poison?**

What do soluble and insoluble mean?

Quite simply, **soluble** means 'will dissolve' and **insoluble** means 'won't dissolve'. If we say that sugar is soluble we mean that sugar will dissolve, and if we say that sand is insoluble we mean that sand won't dissolve.

The mixture of a liquid and the solid dissolved in it is called a solution, so the photograph on the right shows copper sulphate solution.

The solid that dissolves is called the **solute**. In copper sulphate solution, copper sulphate is the solute; in sugar solution, sugar is the solute.

ⓑ **What is the solute in salt solution?**

Sand is insoluble. If sand dissolved in water we would never have any beaches.

Copper sulphate is soluble.

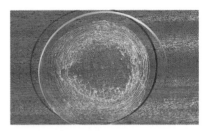

How do you separate the mixture?

A **mixture** is made up of two or more substances that can be separated fairly easily – usually without having to add chemicals.

This means that solutions are mixtures, because you can get the solute back from a solution by heating the solution until the liquid has **evaporated**, which leaves the solute sitting there by itself.

One place you can see this quite easily is in tap water. Many people think that tap water is a pure substance because it has been cleaned and **chlorine** has been added to kill **bacteria**. But in science 'pure' means 'a substance which is not mixed with anything else'. Treated water is still a mixture.

You can see this if you put a small amount of tap water in a shallow dish and leave it somewhere warm (such as on a sunny windowsill) for a few days until the water has evaporated. Any solids dissolved in your sample of tap water will be left behind on the dish.

Using a glass dish makes it easier to see what was in the water.

C **Where has the water gone to?**

Why can't we separate solutions by filtering?

When things are mixed together you can sometimes separate them by **filtering**, but you can't do that with solutions. When something dissolves it is still there, but in very, very small bits, which are too small to see and too small to get stuck in filter paper, so they go straight through.

If you have bits in your liquid that are big enough to see then you will usually be able to get them out by pouring the mixture through filter paper, but you can *never* separate a solution by filtering.

Sand grains are big enough to be stopped by filter paper, but dissolved sugar goes straight through.

QUESTIONS

1 What is the solute in these solutions?
  Salt solution; sugar solution; copper nitrate solution.

2 When a mixture was filtered, it left some substances behind on the filter paper. How do you know that the substances on the filter paper had not dissolved?

3 When scientists say that something is 'pure' what do they mean?

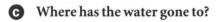

HOW MUCH SALT IS IN THIS ROCK?

Salt crystals

What is salt?

Salt is a chemical whose name is sodium chloride.
This means it is made of two substances, sodium and chlorine.

Where does salt come from?

Salt can be mined from the ground either by digging out lumps of **rock salt** or by pumping water into the salt mine. This dissolves the salt and brings it out of the mine as salt solution, which is also called **brine**.

There are salt mines in Britain – in Cheshire, County Durham and Staffordshire. About seven million tonnes of salt are produced from these mines each year.

Salt is also available from sea water, which contains lots of it. If the sea water is collected and allowed to evaporate, the salt is left behind and can be scraped up and put in boxes. This is what you can buy in the shops as 'sea salt'. This is usually done in hotter countries than Britain.

About 186 million tonnes of salt are produced each year around the world.

Salt pans

What is salt used for?

Many of us sprinkle salt on our chips and other food. This is only one use though. Most of the salt mined in this country is used by the chemical industry to make chlorine (for plastics, **insecticides** and water treatment), sodium hydroxide (for paper, soaps, **detergents**) and in making soap and glass. Salt is also used to make **hard water** soft and to stop ice forming on roads.

Uses of salt

How do we get pure salt from rock salt?

Rock salt is just pure salt with a few extras. As we don't want these extras and they make the salt impure, we call them **impurities**.

To get the salt out of rock salt, we crush it and add water to dissolve the salt. Then we filter the mixture to get rid of the undissolved impurities; then all we have to do is get crystals of pure salt from the salt solution.

ⓐ How do we get crystals of salt from salt solution?

ⓑ The pure salt we have at the end weighs less than the rock salt we started with. Why?

Crushing

Which is the best way to extract salt?

Imagine everyone in your class were given 100g of rock salt and a choice of equipment. If you were told there would be a prize for the person who could get the most pure salt out of their sample of rock salt, how could you set about winning the prize?

There is one plan above, but there are two places in the plan where you would have to be careful not to lose some of your salt by throwing it away.

ⓒ Write down one or more ways in which some of the salt could be lost. *Hint: look at the filtering process.*

ⓓ Now write an improved plan for extracting pure salt from rock salt, using your ideas from **ⓒ**.

Dissolving

Filtering

QUESTIONS

1 Why is salt extracted from seawater mainly in hot countries?

2 Three groups in a different class decided on different ways of getting pure salt from rock salt. The table shows how much rock salt they had and how much pure salt they ended up with.

Group	1	2	3
Amount of rock salt at the start	100 g	200 g	100 g
Amount of pure salt at end	50 g	75 g	30 g

   a Work out what percentage of salt each group got out of their rock salt.

   b Which group had the most effective extraction method?

3 Can you suggest any reason why the competition *might* not be fair?

4 Why can chlorine and chemicals with sodium in them be made from salt?

WHAT HAPPENS TO THE SOLUTE DURING DISSOLVING?

The disappearing solute trick

Where does the solute go to when it dissolves? If you've ever tasted water before and after adding salt to it you'll know the salt is still there. But where? And is it all still there? You could find out if all the salt is still there by doing the following investigation.

Get a beaker, fill it half full of water and weigh it. Let's say the beaker and water together weigh 300 g. Now add 50 g of salt to the water and stir until the salt dissolves.

(a) **Do you think the salt, the water and the beaker altogether will have a mass less than 350 g, exactly 350 g or more than 350 g?**

(300 g of water) + (50 g of salt) = (how much solution?)

If you think the total weight is less than 350 g you are in very good company because most people do. But you are wrong.

When you add 50 g of something to 300 g of something else you always get a total of 350 g. This applies to dissolving as much as to anything else. You have added a solute to the liquid.

Whenever something dissolves, the total mass of the solute and the liquid you add it to stays the same, or is **conserved**.

Applying the particle model

We know that liquids and solids are made of **particles**, so can we apply the particle model of solids, liquids and gases to what is happening when things dissolve?

The answer is that we can. A crystal (or any old lump) of solid salt will break up into very small pieces that are surrounded by water particles. The pieces are too small to see, so the salt seems to disappear.

We can use a scientific **model** to help us understand what goes on when a solute dissolves. There are forces (which are invisible like the force between north and south poles of a magnet) between particles that keep them 'glued' together.

300 g water

50 g salt

Salt solution

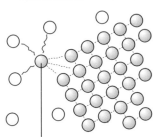
A solute particle is pulled away from a lump of solute.

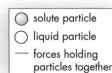

- ⬤ solute particle
- ◯ liquid particle
- — forces holding particles together

There are forces between liquid particles and solute particles.

When substances dissolve, the forces between the liquid particles and the solute particles are stronger than the forces between the solute particles.

This pulls the solute particles apart and then causes the liquid and solute particles to squash together.

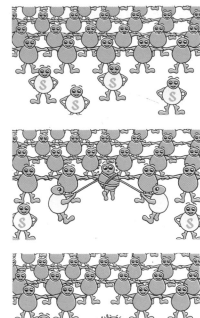

This means that the mixture doesn't take up as much space as you would expect. So, although the *masses* of solute and liquid always add up to the same total whether they are separate or mixed together, their *volumes* don't. For example…

sodium hydroxide   +   water   →   sodium hydroxide solution

5 g	+	95 g	=	100 g	✔
2.3 cm³	+	95.2 cm³	=	94.9 cm³	✗

In this case, the mixture takes up less volume than either of the two substances put into it. Magic? No, science! There are very strong forces involved, pulling particles close together.

Why won't filtering work?

As we mentioned in Topic H1, 'When something dissolves it is still there, but in very, very small bits, which are too small to see and too small to get stuck in filter paper, so they go straight through.'

If you look at the photograph of a greatly magnified view of a piece of filter paper, you can start to understand why some particles (the dissolved ones) can get through filter paper but large clusters of particles just get stuck.

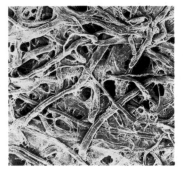

Groups of particles can get trapped by the fibres.

QUESTIONS

1 If you dissolve 25 g of sugar in 75 g of water, what will be the mass of the sugar solution you get?

2 If you have a solution of 50 g of potassium chloride in 200 g of water, what mass of potassium chloride would you end up with if you evaporated all the water?

3 What happens to the solute particles when a crystal of salt dissolves?

4 Draw diagrams to help you explain why a dissolved solid will go through filter paper but a grain of sand will not.

HOW DO WE GET THE SOLVENT BACK FROM A MIXTURE?

TOPIC CHECKLIST

- What is a solvent?
- When is it useful to get the solvent back?
- What is distillation?
- What's going on?

What is a solvent?

A **solvent** is a liquid that will dissolve a solute.

There are lots of solvents, and all of them will dissolve things. Water is only one solvent, but it is so common that as soon as anyone mentions dissolving we assume that they mean 'dissolving in water' so it is important when we talk about dissolving that we say which solvent we are using.

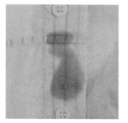

Stain removers contain solvents that will often dissolve oil, grease and tar stains

When is it useful to get the solvent back?

More often than you might think.

If you have sea water but no fresh water you might be extremely interested in getting the solvent out of the sea water, preferably before you died of thirst.

If you need absolutely pure water with nothing at all dissolved in it you need to get the solvent from 'ordinary' water, which has all sorts of other things mixed in with it.

If you want to make whisky from a mixture of barley, water and yeast you need to separate the solvent from the mixture – twice!

What is distillation?

Distillation is the name of the process which is used to get the solvent out of a mixture. Distillation has two steps.

In step 1 the mixture is heated so that the solvent evaporates. The solvent evaporates at a lower temperature than the solute.

In step 2 the evaporated solvent is cooled down so that it **condenses** back into a liquid again.

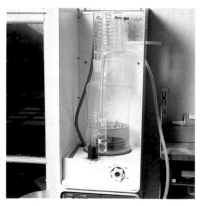

*A water **still***

A solar still for distilling seawater

You may have seen this happen with blue ink, when colourless water is distilled out of it.

Distillation is used to purify water and to make whisky. It can even be used to separate mixtures of liquids into separate liquids, which is how crude oil is separated into useful liquids like paraffin, petrol and heating oil.

What's going on?

When a solution is heated, all the particles in the mixture start to move around faster. When the solvent particles are hot enough they leave the liquid and move into the air.
The solvent is becoming a gas. The change from liquid to gas is called evaporation. When water is the solvent, the gas it forms when it evaporates is water vapour.

The solvent usually all boils off into a gas before the solute comes near to boiling. For example, if you heat salt solution, the water boils when it reaches 100 °C but the salt doesn't even melt until it gets to a temperature of 801 °C and doesn't boil until it reaches 1413 °C.

When the gas is cooled down, its particles slow down again and get closer together, so that the solvent soon turns back into a liquid again. This can be collected by letting it drip into a beaker.

There are lots of different ways of cooling the water vapour down. The Liebig condenser in the photograph on the right cools the tube carrying the water vapour, by surrounding it with cold water. The cold water is better than air at removing heat from the water vapour.

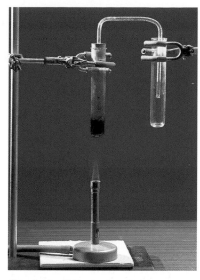

Separating blue ink by distillation

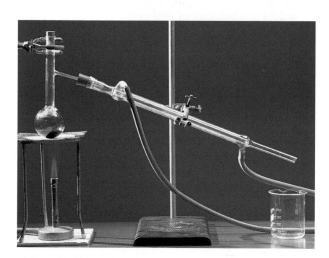

Using a Liebig condenser

QUESTIONS

1 Give one reason for wanting to get the solvent back from a solution.

2 What is a solvent?

3 What are the two changes involved in distillation?

4 Explain how distillation separates a solvent from a solute.

5 At what temperature would salt become

   a   a liquid?   b   a gas?

6 Draw particle diagrams to show how the arrangement of particles in the solvent change as it becomes a gas.

USING CHROMATOGRAPHY TO SEPARATE MIXTURES

TOPIC CHECKLIST

● When do we use chromatography for separation?

● How does chromatography work?

● How is chromatography used?

When do we use chromatography for separation?

Chromatography is another way of finding out whether a liquid is a pure substance or a mixture of substances.

If you have a mixture of two or more different solutes in the same solvent, evaporating a solution of the mixture will just give you the mixture back again. Chromatography allows you to separate the different solutes.

How does chromatography work?

Most inks are mixtures of different coloured dyes. Chromatography can prove this by splitting the mixture up.

ⓐ **How many coloured dyes is this ink made up of and what are they?**

How does letting a solvent move past a mixture split the mixture up? The solvent 'sticks' to the particles of the solutes in the mixture, and then carries them along as it moves.

The particles of some solutes stick more strongly to the paper than others, so they are not carried as far before they are dropped. If you are patient enough to watch closely you can see evidence of this happening – the bands of colour separate very slowly. The result is a **chromatogram**, or 'colour picture'.

Put one drop of ink in the middle of a filter paper. Allow the ink to dry and then add another drop in exactly the same place. Repeat with another three drops.

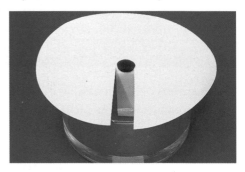

When the ink is dry, cut a wick or tongue of paper as shown in the picture. Rest the paper on top of a suitable container of solvent so that the wick just dips in to the solvent.

The solvent slowly soaks up the wick and then spreads out across the paper, carrying the dyes in the ink along with it. After a few minutes you can see the coloured dyes separating from each other.

How is chromatography used?

Chromatography can be used to analyse foods to see what is in them.

The colours on the outside of a Smartie can be separated by chromatography. Wet a small paint brush and wipe it across a Smartie – effectively 'unpainting' the Smartie! Put the drops of colour from the Smartie near the bottom of a rectangular piece of filter paper and carry out the chromatography by putting one edge of the filter paper into the solvent. This makes the colour spread straight up the paper, so you can put different blobs next to each other to compare them.

Yellow Smarties contain a tiny amount of a yellow food colouring. The chromatogram on the right shows four yellow dyes and the colour from a yellow Smartie. If the Smartie blobs line up sideways with the blobs from one of the yellow dyes, that is the dye that is in the Smartie.

Chromatography can also be used to detect small amounts of substances in a complex mixture.

When athletes have a **urine** test, chromatography is used to separate the mixture of chemicals in their urine. The separated chemicals are analysed to see if any of them are 'banned substances' which could make the athletes perform better. If the athlete is banned from sport because of drug taking, it could ruin their career, so this testing has to be 100% accurate.

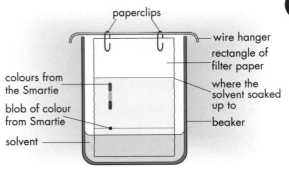

Apparatus to compare chromatograms

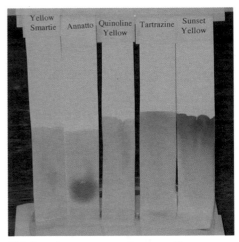

This is a chromatogram from a yellow coloured Smartie and four food colours. When complete, the Smartie colours can be compared with those in the food colourings.

QUESTIONS

1 When would you use chromatography to separate two or more substances instead of filtering or distillation?

2 Look at the chromatogram on the right. Which dyes (of a, b, c and d) are in substance X?

3 Why do some solutes travel further up the filter paper than others during chromatography?

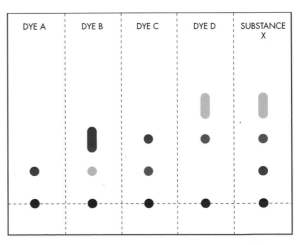

Chromatogram for question 2

WHAT AFFECTS DISSOLVING?

Do things dissolve in different solvents?

Some solutes dissolve in one solvent and some will dissolve in others, but many solutes will dissolve in more than one solvent.

For example, sulphur is insoluble in water but will dissolve in alcohol, while salt will dissolve in water and in alcohol.

How much can dissolve?

Different solutes can dissolve in the same solvent, but different amounts of each solute will dissolve. For example 36 g of salt will dissolve in water at room temperature, but 65 g of potassium bromide could dissolve in the same amount of water. We say that potassium bromide is more soluble than salt.

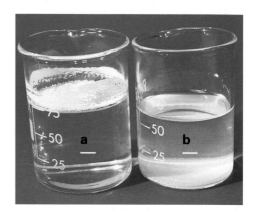

Sulphur in (a) water and (b) alcohol

What is a saturated solution?

A **saturated solution** is a solution that has dissolved so much solute that it can't dissolve any more. The amount of solute needed to make the solution saturated depends on the solvent, the solute and the temperature. You can tell when a solution is saturated because if you add more solute it falls to the bottom and won't dissolve no matter how long you stir it.

Scientists call this the **solubility** of the solute.

What difference does temperature make?

It is pretty obvious that temperature affects *how quickly* the solute dissolves – sugar dissolves better in a hot cup of tea than in a cold one. The temperature of the solvent also affects *how much* solute dissolves in it.

Use the table to answer these questions.

a How much copper sulphate dissolves in water at 20 °C?

b How much copper sulphate dissolves in water at 60 °C?

Temperature of solvent (°C)	Amount of copper sulphate that can dissolve in 100 cm³ of water (g)
0	14
20	21
40	29
60	40
80	55

Pupils in a Year 7 class carried out the experiment below to find out how much difference temperature makes, to how much solute can dissolve. Each of the six groups did the experiment in the same way, except that they had different amounts of solute.

Each group added all its solute to the water in the boiling tube, then put the tube in a beaker of warm water to let the tube cool down very slowly.

The pupils wrote down the temperature when the first crystals appeared in the tube. The solution was saturated, so they knew how much solute made a saturated solution at that temperature.

Their results are shown in the table below.

c Plot a line graph of the results with temperature on the bottom axis and amount of solute on the side axis.

Writing down the solubility

To write down the solubility of a substance, you need:

● The amount and name of the solute

● The volume, name and temperature of the solvent

For example, 35.7 g of salt will dissolve in 100 cm³ of water at 0 °C.

d The solubility of potassium nitrate is 247 g per 100 cm³ of water at 100 °C. How much potassium nitrate will dissolve in 200 cm³ of water at 100 °C?

e What is the solubility of copper sulphate
a) in 100 cm³ of water at 40 °C?
b) in 10 cm³ of water at 40 °C?

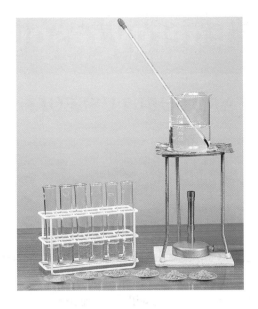

Cooling the solution

Crystals forming

Temperature at which solution is saturated (°C)	Amount of solute in 10 cm³ of water (g)
0	1.4
20	2.1
40	2.9
60	4.0
80	5.5
100	7.5

QUESTIONS

1 How much more salt can you dissolve in a saturated solution of salt?

2 What happens to the amount of solute which will dissolve as the temperature increases?

3 What is the effect of temperature on the solubility of copper sulphate?

4 What is the solubility of copper sulphate at 70 °C?

Energy resources

11   WHY ARE FUELS USEFUL?

Why do we burn fuels?

We burn **fuels** for the heat and light they give us. Both heat and light are forms of energy.

Some of the more common fuels are gas, oil and coal. When fuels burn they produce carbon dioxide and water vapour, but the important thing for us is the energy we get from them.

a   **What other materials can you burn as fuels?**

What is energy?

Energy makes things happen. The heat from burning fuels can cook our food and warm our homes.

Energy can take many forms, and it can **transform** from one form to another. The energy itself does not change – just the form you use it in. A fuel is a store of energy and when it burns the stored energy is **transformed** to heat and light energy.

The heat energy produced by fuels can be transformed again to different forms. In a car, the heat energy released by burning petrol is transformed in the engine to movement energy to drive the car.

In power stations, the heat energy produced by fuels is turned into movement energy which is used to turn turbines, which transform the movement energy into electrical energy.

So whatever you do, you need energy to do it! This includes our own bodies. We get energy from our food and use it in everything we do. So when we run for a bus we are transforming the energy we get from food into movement energy in our muscles.

heat from engine   petrol is fuel   movement energy →

A car engine burns fuel with oxygen from the air to produce heat. The heat is used to move the car.

Turbines

runner gets hot

energy from food

The runner gains movement energy.

Energy does not just come from fuels. Our greatest source of light and heat energy is from the Sun. Wind and waves have a great deal of movement energy which we can use.

Measuring ~~heat energy~~ Temperature.

When a substance gains heat energy it gets hotter. We call the hotness of something its **temperature**. The most common device for measuring the temperature of a substance is a **thermometer**.

How do we use a thermometer?

Using a thermometer is fairly simple, but there are some basic rules to follow.

- If you are measuring the temperature of a liquid, always stir the liquid gently to avoid measuring the temperature of hot or cold spots.

- Do not take the thermometer out of the liquid to read it because as soon as you do, the reading will change.

- Always make sure the thermometer is safe because the glass body of the thermometer is easily broken.

- Check that you know what each division on the thermometer means.

- Always wear goggles to avoid liquids getting into your eyes.

Keep the thermometer in the liquid while reading the temperature.

How do thermometer scales work?

All thermometers have the 10 degree Celsius intervals marked on. Some thermometers have every $\frac{1}{2}$ a degree marked, some every degree and some every other degree. As a general rule, look to see how many divisions each 10°C is divided into. This will help you understand what the scale means.

b Both of the thermometer scales below on the right show the same temperature, 57°C. Explain how this is so.

c Sketch a thermometer scale that reads 49°C.

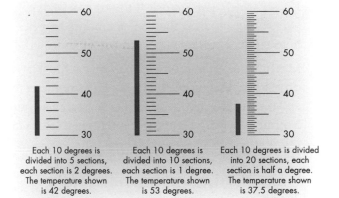

Each 10 degrees is divided into 5 sections, each section is 2 degrees. The temperature shown is 42 degrees.

Each 10 degrees is divided into 10 sections, each section is 1 degree. The temperature shown is 53 degrees.

Each 10 degrees is divided into 20 sections, each section is half a degree. The temperature shown is 37.5 degrees.

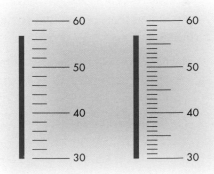

QUESTIONS

1 What two forms of energy are produced when a fuel burns?

2 Describe the difference between a fuel and energy.

3 List the 4 forms of energy described on these pages.

USING ENERGY SOURCES IN SCIENCE EXPERIMENTS

Which fuel is best?

We can test different fuels to see how much heat energy they give us. To do this we can use them to heat up water.

How well does a Bunsen burner heat?

One fuel which we have plenty of in a science laboratory is gas. We can test how much heat this type of fuel gives by using a Bunsen burner.

Set up a Bunsen burner on a heat mat with a beaker containing 200 ml of cold water on a tripod and gauze.

Decide which flame to use. If the air hole on the Bunsen is open you will get a roaring flame. For a more gentle heat, close the air hole a little. The flame will be quiet.

Measure the temperature of the water at the start of the experiment then use a stirring rod thermometer to stir and measure the temperature of the water every minute for 5 minutes. Record the measurements in a results table like this one.

Using a Bunsen burner safely

- Always wear eye protection.
- Always wear a lab coat and tie your hair back.
- Check that there are no holes or splits in the Bunsen's rubber tubing.
- Make sure that the objects you are about to heat are secure.

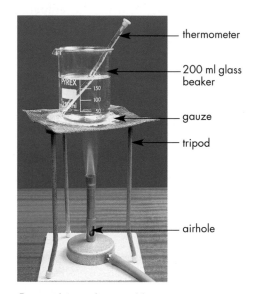

Bunsen burner in use with roaring blue flame

Table 1: Results for the heating effect of a roaring Bunsen flame heating 200 ml of water

Time (mins)	Temperature (°C)
0	18
1	24
2	35
3	45
4	56
5	67

Not only the things you want to heat get hot. Tripods, gauzes and beakers can be hot too. Be careful; treat an object as though it is hot unless you know otherwise.

When you are not using the Bunsen burner always close the air hole. The yellow flame is much more visible than the blue flame.

Comparing fuels

What results would we get from a different type of fuel? The gas we use in Bunsen burners is not the most convenient type of fuel because it is difficult to carry around. If you were going camping you might take a form of solid fuel which is easy to carry. But how much heat would this give compared to a Bunsen burner?

If you repeated the experiment using some solid camping fuel in a foil pie case, you might get results like the ones on the right. You can put these results with the Bunsen burner results on a graph to compare the two fuels.

(a) **Why is it important to use the same amount of water for each experiment?**

(b) **Why is it important to record your results over the same amount of time?**

(c) **Why do you take the temperature of the water before you start?**

(d) **From the graph of solid fuel and Bunsen burner heating results, say which fuel is better and explain why you say this.**

(e) **Heating effect is not the only quality of a fuel – what else is important when you are choosing a fuel?**

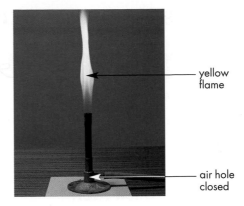

Bunsen burner with yellow flame (air hole closed)

Table 2: Results of heating 200 ml of water using solid fuel

Time (mins)	Temperature (°C)
0	18
1	19
2	20
3	21
4	22
5	23

QUESTIONS

1 Explain how to control the type of Bunsen flame.

2 When is it important to use a safety flame?

3 What safety equipment must be worn when conducting experiments using heat?

4 The table shows the results of heating water using a spirit burner:

   a Copy the table on the right and add the results for the Bunsen burner and the solid fuel.

   b Which fuel gives most heat?

Table 3

Time (mins)	Temperature (°C)
0	18
1	20
2	23
3	25
4	27
5	28

WHAT ARE FOSSIL FUELS?

What is a fossil fuel?

A fossil is the remains of an animal or plant that has been preserved for millions of years. A **fossil fuel** is one which was formed from the bodies of animals and plants that lived hundreds of millions of years ago.

Because fossil fuels took so long to form, they cannot be replaced once they have been burned. It would take more millions of years to form more fossil fuels. As they cannot be renewed we call them **non-renewable** or **capital** resources.

Coal

Coal is a black solid found underground. It is the remains of the huge forests which covered much of the Earth around 300 million years ago. There were no humans around to cut them down and haul them off as logs so when they died they just lay where they fell, often into huge swamps. Over millions of years rocks formed over them which squashed them down into coal.

Crude oil

Crude oil is a sticky black liquid found deep underground. It was formed many millions of years ago at the bottom of the sea, from the bodies of tiny organisms that lived in the sea. If they were trapped under rock, over millions of years they became oil.

Crude oil (or **mineral** oil) can be separated into many useful fuels. These include petrol, paraffin and diesel.

Gas

Natural gas is a colourless gas formed along with crude oil at the bottom of the sea millions of years ago. It is a very useful fuel because it burns very easily and is easily piped around the country to homes and industries.

Coal

Crude oil

Natural gas

Using fossil fuels

Humans have been on the Earth for about two million years and during most of that time they hardly used fossil fuels. Fossil fuels are usually underground and so are hard to get out. The main fuel for thousands of years was wood, or peat, which forms on top of the Earth. Animal oil was also used for lamps.

Coal is the easiest to dig out from underground. People used this as an energy resource for hundreds of years but not much until the nineteenth century. Oil and gas were not produced or used much until the twentieth century.

Once we started using fossil fuels we used them in a big way. Most of what we do depends on coal, oil and gas. In the nineteenth century coal was used in steam engines which provided energy for factories and mines as well as trains. In the twentieth century coal also provided energy for the first electricity generating stations.

By the end of the twentieth century oil and gas were more commonly used than coal. Oil can be used to make petrol for cars and the plastics which we use every day. Gas and oil make cleaner fuels than coal which produces a lot of ash and smoke when it burns. In some countries coal is starting to run out after so many years of use.

Table: UK energy usage (millions of tons of oil equivalent)

Year	Coal	Oil	Gas
1970	99	95	4
1980	78	78	46
1990	65	80	54
2000	35	77	96

a Use the data on the right to plot a graph of the use of coal, oil and gas over the last 30 years.

b Think about your everyday life. Start when you get up in the morning and make a list of all the fossil fuels you rely on during the day (don't forget that although electricity isn't a fuel, most electricity is produced by burning fossil fuels).

Using fuel in the future

We don't know when gas, oil and coal will run out. All we know is that they will some day. So we have two choices. One is to use less so that they last longer. The other is to use some other energy resource.

c Think about your day again. How could you use less fossil fuel? (e.g. walking or going by bus instead of using a car, switching lights off.)

QUESTIONS

1 Why are fossil fuels running out?

2 Why are fossil fuels 'non-renewable'?

3 Wood is not a fossil fuel. Why not?

4 Why do you think that oil has replaced coal as the energy resource for transport?

WHAT ARE RENEWABLE ENERGY RESOURCES?

TOPIC CHECKLIST

- What does renewable mean?
- What are the main types of renewable energy resources?
- What factors affect the performance of solar panels?

What does renewable mean?

Renewable energy resources are those which do not get smaller if you use them. For example, collecting energy from sunlight does not change the amount of energy arriving on the Earth's surface from the Sun. This makes renewable energy resources very attractive, because they can't be used up.

What are the main types of renewable energy resources?

Energy from water

We can use the energy from the movement of fast flowing water to make electricity. The electricity is made by **hydroelectric** power stations in mountain areas. This is because it is easy to get a good fast downhill flow of water on a mountain which will turn the turbines in the station.

Energy from the Earth

The inside of the Earth is very hot and in some areas such as Iceland this heat is close to the surface. It heats water below the ground and this can be used to generate electricity and provide heating. Energy taken from the heat of the Earth in this way is called **geothermal** energy.

Energy from plants

Biomass is the name given to plant material burnt as a fuel. As long as the number of new plants growing is the same as the number burned, this fuel source is renewable.

Energy from waves

The energy in waves from the sea can be used to make electricity. This is a bit unpredictable as the size of waves depends on the weather. High winds produce large waves which have a lot of movement energy.

Energy from wind

In some places giant windmills are used to make electricity using the movement energy from the wind. This also depends on the weather!

A hydroelectric dam

Geothermal springs

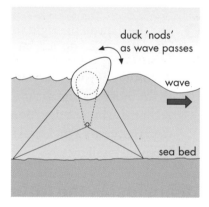
Wave power

Wind turbines

Energy direct from the Sun

Energy direct from the Sun (**solar** energy) is one of the best renewable energy resources as it can be used anywhere. The big drawback to solar power is the unpredictable amount of sunlight, and, of course, night-time.

Solar cells can transfer energy from the Sun's heat and light to electrical energy. This happens in many electronic devices such as calculators and watches. Equipment which needs electrical energy but is far away from a generator, like space stations or buoys out at sea, also use solar cells.

Solar panels, which heat water for central heating systems, are becoming an increasingly common sight.

What factors affect the performance of solar panels?

Size is important – the larger the energy-collecting surface, the more energy can be collected. But colour is also important. The experiment below is designed to find out which is the best colour for solar panels.

- Pour 30 ml of cold water into each of two balloons and measure the temperature of the water in each balloon.
- Place both balloons in sunlight or lit by a lamp. Take care that they both get the same amount of light.
- Put a white cloth over one balloon and a black cloth over the other.
- Measure the temperature of the balloons every 4 minutes and record the temperatures in a chart like Table 1.

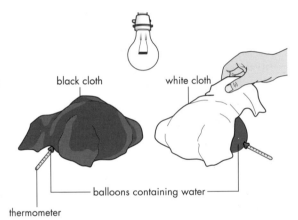

black cloth   white cloth

balloons containing water

thermometer

Table 1

Time (mins)	Temperatures (°C)	
	White cloth	Black cloth
0	18	18
4	20	21
8	23	26
12	26	30
16	28	33
20	31	35

a Which balloon has warmer water after 20 minutes?

b Which colour would you use for a solar panel?

c Why is it important to measure the volumes of water in each balloon?

d What other factors could affect the rate at which the temperature changes?

QUESTIONS

1 Only one of the renewable energy resources on these pages is a fuel. Which one and why is it a fuel?

2 For each renewable energy resource on these pages, write a sentence saying what sort of place you would have to live in to be able to use it.

HOW DO LIVING THINGS USE ENERGY?

TOPIC CHECKLIST

- Where do we get our energy from?
- How much energy is there in food?
- Which foods store the most energy?

Where do we get our energy from?

Living things need energy for movement, growth, and just standing still! Even while we are asleep, our heart is still pumping and our lungs are breathing and all this needs energy.

Animals get their energy from food, which can be other animals or plants. Plants make their own food using energy from sunlight.

The type and amount of energy we take into our bodies through food is important. If we eat too little, our bodies cannot carry on the vital life processes. If we eat too much, our bodies store the excess energy as fat. A limited store of energy in the form of fat is a good idea, but being too fat can cause health problems, just as being too thin can.

How much energy is there in food?

Our bodies process food in a very similar way to burning. The food is combined with oxygen, which releases the energy. We can find out how much energy is stored in food by burning it.

Energy is measured in **joules**; 1 joule is quite a small amount of energy. Lifting objects on the Earth requires energy, lifting an apple a distance of 1 metre transfers about 1 joule of energy.

Which foods store the most energy?

To find out which foods store the most energy, a simple experiment can be carried out, similar to the experiment we saw on fuels earlier.

- Pour 10 ml of water into a boiling tube, held in a clamp.
- Measure the temperature of the water with a stirring rod thermometer.
- Place a sample of food on a metal dish on a tripod. 1 gram of sugar works well.

A mountaineer uses a lot of energy.

We use energy even when we are asleep.

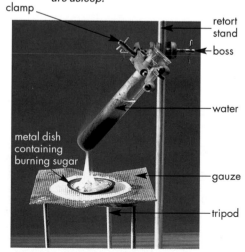

clamp
retort stand
boss
water
metal dish containing burning sugar
gauze
tripod

Finding the energy in sugar

- Heat the dish with a strong Bunsen flame until the food catches light. Then remove the Bunsen flame from the food.

- Hold the boiling tube so that the bottom end is in the flames from the food, until the flames go out.

- Measure the temperature of the water in the boiling tube.

Try equal masses of different foods. The bigger the temperature rise of the water, the more stored energy the food had.

1 gram of sugar raised the temperature of 10 ml of water by 27°C.

ⓐ Why do you hold the boiling tube over the food only when the Bunsen has been removed?

ⓑ Do you think that all of the energy stored in the burning foods is transferred to the water?

Many foods carry labels which show how much energy is contained in the food. Chocolate has a large amount of energy stored in it. The food label on the right shows how much energy is contained in the chocolate.

ⓒ If lifting an apple 1 metre needs 1 joule of energy, how far would the energy in the chocolate lift the apple?

A famous scientist, John Tyndall, calculated that the energy stored in a ham sandwich was enough to lift him to the top of the Matterhorn, a mountain in Switzerland. Mr. Tyndall then set off up the Matterhorn with just a ham sandwich. He got very hungry! What he should have taken into account is the energy our bodies need to keep living, even if we don't move. Also when it is cold, our bodies 'burn' a lot of 'fuel' keeping us warm.

ⓓ Why does a mountaineer have to eat much more than one ham sandwich to climb a mountain?

Result
The heat from burning 1 gram of sugar warmed 10 ml of water from 18°C to 45°C

Ingredients: milk, sugar, cocoa mass, cocoa butter, vegetable fat, emulsifier: E442, flavourings.

Nutrition Information		Per Bag	Per 100 g
Energy	kJ	900	2195
	kcal	215	525
Protein	g	3.2	7.8
Carbohydrate	g	23.3	56.8
Fat	g	12.1	29.4

MILK SOLIDS 20% MINIMUM, COCOA SOLIDS 20% MINIMUM.

Table 1: Daily energy requirements

Age and activity	Energy needed each day (kJ)
Child 8 years	8000
Active teenage female	11800
Active teenage male	14700
Adult resting	7600
Active adult female	8800
Active adult male	10500

QUESTIONS

1 Where does energy for life come from?

2 Explain why, even if you are asleep, your body is transferring and using energy.

3 Look at the table on the right. Explain the difference in energy needs of an 8 year old child and an active teenager. Suggest how their diets might need to be different.

Where does the energy in food come from?

We have seen that food is full of stored energy. But where does it come from? The answer is the Sun. Plants make their own food by using light energy from the Sun, water and carbon dioxide. The plant itself becomes a store of energy. When animals eat plants this energy is transferred to the animals.

 →  →

Grass → *Cow* → *Human*

A food chain shows this flow of energy from plants to animals, and sometimes on to other animals. Look at the three photos above. The arrows show which way the energy flows in the food chain.

ⓐ **Complete the food chain**   grass → .... → fox

ⓑ **Why could we say we live on sunshine?**

Why does most of our energy come from the Sun?

All of the energy we get from fossil fuels originally came from the Sun. Fossil fuels are made of the remains of plants and animals which were alive millions of years ago.

 →  →  →

Sun   *Plants*   *Fossil fuels*   *Car*
light energy   *stored energy*   *(petrol) stored energy*   *movement energy*

Some renewable resources, like wood and other biomass fuels, are plants which have used and stored the Sun's energy. Others like wind, come from the complicated weather patterns driven partly by the Sun's heat.

ⓒ **Draw a diagram to show how the Sun's energy from millions of years ago can be transferred to electricity today.**

How can we use energy well?

Humans use more of the Earth's energy resources now than ever in our history. There are more of us than ever before but also the way we live demands more energy, especially in rich areas such as Europe and North America.

Burning fossil fuels causes pollution. Scientists now think that the amount of carbon dioxide from burning fossil fuels is making the Earth warm up. This is melting the ice at the poles of the Earth, raising sea levels and causing flooding. Global warming is also changing weather patterns, which causes more rain and makes rivers burst their banks. The coal mines, oil and gas wells often make a mess of the land around them, and oil spills have killed millions of animals.

Renewable energy resources will not run out and they produce far less pollution than burning fossil fuels. But they are often unpredictable and do not yet produce enough energy to replace fossil fuels. Many renewable energy resources would take up large areas of land. You need a lot of windmills to make up for one gas-powered electricity generating station.

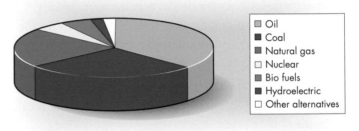

- ☐ Oil
- ■ Coal
- ■ Natural gas
- ☐ Nuclear
- ■ Bio fuels
- ■ Hydroelectric
- ☐ Other alternatives

Energy production from fossil fuels and alternatives

We know that fossil fuels will run out at some point. What do you think we should be doing to make sure that we still have the energy we need in the future?

d Here are some ideas. Read and discuss them with a partner or in a group and then write a paragraph saying what you think we should do.

We should use more solar power – the Sun's energy is everywhere.

Why carry on using up fossil fuels when we've got the wind and waves?

We could all use cars running on electricity – they're slower but cleaner.

The rich countries use far more of the Earth's resources than the poor ones – they should be the ones cutting back.

QUESTIONS

1 Draw a food chain/energy chain to show how energy gets from plants to an anteater.

2 Explain how the energy in oil came from the Sun.

3 Explain why putting less water in a kettle to make a cup of tea helps us use less energy.

J Electrical circuits

J1 HOW DO ELECTRICAL CIRCUITS WORK?

TOPIC CHECKLIST

- When does current flow?
- How do we draw circuit diagrams?

When does current flow?

Electricity flows in a very similar way to water flowing through pipes or blood flowing around your body. In the same way as water and blood need a route to flow along, electricity needs a material that it can flow through. Materials that electricity can flow through are called **conductors**.

A complete route from one end of a cell to the other is called a **circuit**.

In an electrical circuit, the cell pushes electricity and makes it flow.

ⓐ What organ pushes blood around your body?

Electricity flowing in a circuit is called **electric current**.

You can tell when your central heating is working because the radiator gets hot.

You can tell when the electric circuit is working because the bulb lights up.

In a central heating system, water moves around in pipes. If one of the pipes is blocked, this will stop the water moving in the whole system.

For the bulb to light in a simple circuit, there must be a complete circuit for the current to flow through and a cell to provide energy to the circuit.

In a simple circuit, if the current is stopped from flowing in one place in the circuit, then it will be stopped from flowing in the whole circuit. We can stop or start the current flowing in a circuit by using a **switch**. When a switch is open it breaks the circuit. When it is closed the circuit is complete again.

A cell provides energy to electric circuits.

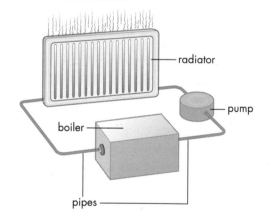

In the central heating system shown above, the pump moves water.

A simple electrical circuit

ⓑ Of the circuits below which one will work?

ⓒ Why will the others not work?

How do we draw circuit diagrams?

To make it easier for us to draw electric circuits, we use a set of simple drawings called **symbols** to show (or represent) each part (**component**) in the circuit.

Symbol	—	+‖–	⌐•⁄	—•—	—⊗—
Component Name	Wire	Cell	Open switch	Closed switch	Bulb

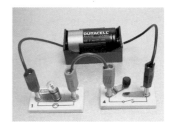

The photograph on the right shows a bulb, a switch and a cell. Below the photograph is a drawing using component symbols, this type of drawing is called a **circuit diagram**.

ⓓ The switch in this circuit is open. Is the light on or off?

ⓔ The photographs below show some different circuits. Draw a circuit diagram for each one.

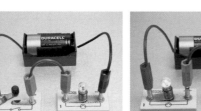   

QUESTIONS

1 Draw the symbols for these components: cell, bulb, wire.

2 What does the cell do in a circuit?

3 How does a switch turn the current on and off?

WHAT HAPPENS IN A CIRCUIT?

TOPIC CHECKLIST

- What happens to electric current as it flows around a simple circuit?
- How is current measured?
- What affects current flow?
- What is resistance?

What happens to electric current as it flows around a simple circuit?

The short answer is 'Not a lot'.

The same amount of current flows into the negative end of the cell as flows out of the positive end of the cell. To help understand this, think of the flow of water in a central heating system. The pump doesn't make water – it just pushes it along.

How is current measured?

Current is measured in **amperes** named after a French scientist. Amperes is often shortened to amps or A. Amps is the name for the unit of electric current.

A bulb is a current indicator. If a big current flows then the bulb is bright. If a small current flows then the bulb is dim. To measure current accurately an **ammeter** is used. An ammeter measures the current flowing *through* it.

The red terminal on the ammeter is connected nearest to the + on the cell, battery or power supply.

In the circuit diagram on the right an ammeter is placed in a circuit and measures the current flowing. If the ammeter were placed somewhere else in the circuit, then the reading would be the same. This is because current at all places in a simple circuit is the same.

This type of circuit where there is only one route that current can take is called a **series** circuit.

ⓐ Which part of an electric circuit behaves like the pump in a heating system?

ⓑ If two bulbs were connected in a series circuit, what would be the effect if one bulb broke?

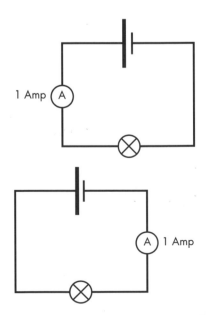

What affects current flow?

Increasing current flow

A cell pushes electric current around a circuit. If there are two cells then more current will flow.

This is very like putting a more powerful pump in your central heating system. The bigger pump will push more water around the system every second which means that a larger current of water is flowing through a radiator.

In the circuit diagrams on the right the circuit with two cells will light the bulbs more brightly because more current flows than with one cell.

Reducing current flow

The radiators in a central heating system are full of twists and turns and this limits the flow of water. If you add more twists and turns it is more difficult for the water to flow and the current flow gets less.

Bulbs allow electric current to flow through them, but they have resistance. When the current has to flow through two bulbs, less current flows than if it only has to flow through one bulb. So the bulbs are less bright than if there was only one bulb.

What is resistance?

The effect of bulbs on current flow, or the bends in radiators on water flow, is called **resistance**.

Resistance is a measure of how difficult it is for the current to flow through something.
~~All~~ *Many* materials allow some current to flow through them but some have much higher resistance than others. If it is easy for the current to flow they are called conductors. ~~If it is difficult for the current to flow they are called insulators.~~

If no current flows, then the material is an insulator.

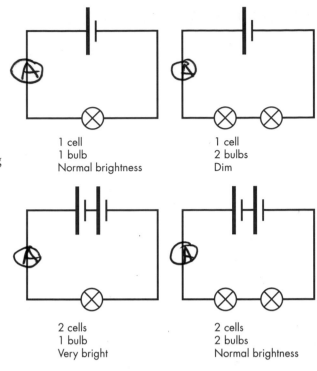

1 cell
1 bulb
Normal brightness

1 cell
2 bulbs
Dim

2 cells
1 bulb
Very bright

2 cells
2 bulbs
Normal brightness

QUESTIONS

1 What is one way of making a bulb glow brighter?

2 What is the name for a circuit when there is only one route around it?

3 What would happen to the current in a simple circuit if a bulb with a higher resistance were used?

4 Why doesn't it matter where you measure the current in a simple circuit?

5 Why does more current flow when more cells are used?

What is a fault?

In electric circuits a fault is anything that stops the circuit from working in the way it should. This could mean that no current will flow or even that too much current will flow.

Finding a fault

There are two ways to find a fault:

- Replace each component to see if it is stopping the circuit working.

- Test each component to see if it is working properly.

Replacing each component can be expensive and if there is more than one fault in the circuit, this method may not work.

Testing each component is a slower but more reliable method. Remember that the wires that connect the components together will need to be tested too.

It is often useful to use both methods together.

My torch doesn't work

When a torch doesn't work there are a number of faults that could be the cause.

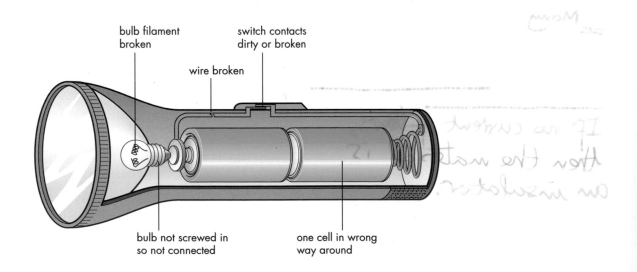

bulb filament broken

switch contacts dirty or broken

wire broken

bulb not screwed in so not connected

one cell in wrong way around

How are individual components tested?

The best way to test a component is to put it in a circuit that you know is working. In the photograph on the right, the working bulb is about to be replaced with the bulb to be tested. If the new test bulb does not light, you know it is faulty. To check, put the working bulb back into the circuit and this bulb should light up again. This makes sure that the test circuit is still working.

In this type of circuit there are only two possible types of fault:

- The cell is not working
- There is a break in the circuit.

A break in the circuit could be anything from a 'blown' bulb filament to a poor contact between the cell and a wire.

What is a short circuit?

If a conductor is connected either side of a component, it provides a short cut for the electric current. This is called a **short circuit**. In the diagram on the right, the short circuit would stop the switch from being able to turn the bulb off.

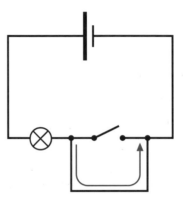

Current will flow even when switch is open.

ⓐ **Why will these circuits not work?**

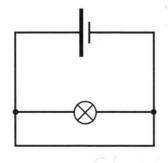
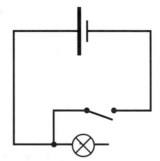
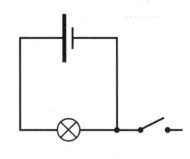

QUESTIONS

1 What is the filament of a bulb made from?

2 Why is it important to keep a torch in a dry clean place?

3 Why is the switch often faulty in an old torch?

4 What would be the most effective method to test for a broken wire in a circuit?

CELLS, BATTERIES AND ELECTRIC CURRENTS

TOPIC CHECKLIST

- What is a cell?
- What is a battery?
- What happens to energy in an electrical circuit?
- What is the difference between current and energy?

What is a cell?

A **cell** is a chemical source of energy. It is this energy which pushes the current around the circuit. It is also this energy which makes the bulb light up.

As chemicals react inside the cell they make electric current flow in a circuit. Once all the chemicals have reacted, they cannot react again and the cell stops working.

People use a range of words for this including: dead, flat, spent, run out. The chemicals in a flat cell will eventually start to leak. The sticky liquid that leaks can damage electrical equipment and is very harmful to people.

The push which a cell or battery supplies is measured in **volts**. The higher the voltage of a battery, the more it pushes the current.

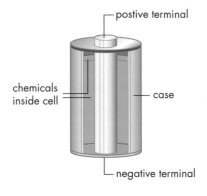

Cell

What is a battery?

A **battery** is two or more cells connected together in series. Torches have a battery of cells with the positive end of one connected to the negative end of the next. It is important to get the cells the right way round or the torch will not work.

Polarity

Both cells and batteries push electric current around circuits. They push the current in one direction, so it is important to get the cell the right way round, so the current flows in the direction you want it to. Each cell has a positive end and a negative end; these are called **poles**. The word **polarity** is used when we examine which end is which and look at the direction of current flow.

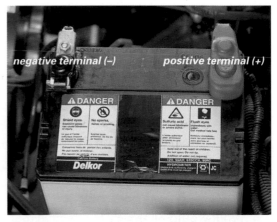

Battery

What happens to energy in an electrical circuit?

When the chemicals in a cell react they release energy which makes the current flow. Electric current is flowing particles called **electrons**. Electrical energy is moved around the circuit by the flow of electrons.

Pushed by the cell, the moving electrons carry electrical energy as they travel around the circuit. When they reach a bulb, some of the energy is passed on to it and turned (transformed) into heat and light energy.

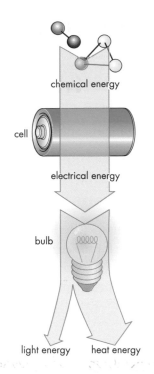

chemical energy

cell

electrical energy

bulb

light energy   heat energy

What is the difference between current and energy?

It is important to get electric current and energy clear in your mind. Because both are invisible it is difficult to imagine how they work. To help understand it we can use a model made of things we can see, like marbles.

Imagine a tube full of marbles. Each marble is the same as all the other marbles in the tube. Someone turns a handle to push the marbles around the tube circuit. As the marbles pass through the paddle wheel they turn the wheel.

Energy is put into the marble system by somebody turning a handle. Energy is transmitted by the flow of marbles to the paddle wheel. The paddle wheel transforms the marble flow into paddle movement. In this circuit the flow of marbles is the same at all points in the circuit.

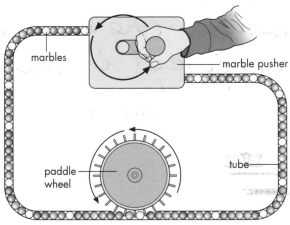

marbles

marble pusher

paddle wheel

tube

It takes both the energy of the handle turner and the flow of marbles to turn the paddle wheel just as it takes the energy from a cell and the flow of electrons to light a bulb.

a What is the 'current' in this model?

b In the marble circuit, which component is like the light bulb?

c What keeps the marbles moving?

d If the person turning the handle stopped, what would happen to the paddle wheel?

QUESTIONS

1 What is the name of the type of energy stored in a cell?

2 What device transforms electrical energy to light energy?

3 How does energy get from a battery to a bulb in a circuit?

4 When a cell starts supplying energy to a circuit the bulb lights up immediately. Use the marble model to help you explain this.

PARALLEL CIRCUITS

TOPIC CHECKLIST

- What happens when the circuit isn't simple?
- What happens in parallel circuits?
- Do models always work?

What happens when the circuit isn't simple?

Up to this point we have looked at simple circuits, where there is only one route for the current to flow along. When there is more than one way around a circuit, the circuit is branched or split. Where this happens, a **parallel** circuit is formed.

Extra current can flow through the extra pipe (connected in parallel) so that a bigger flows through the Battery. 1l

To help understand what is going on in the parallel circuits, we can use a model of water flowing along pipes.

If ~~two litres~~ of water flows into the left end of the pipe, then ~~two litres~~ must flow out of the right. But what happens to the flow in between?

The flow splits and some flows down one branch of the pipe and some flows down the other branch. The two flows then join up again and form a current the same size as before the split happened.

Reword — say 1l through each ∴ 2l in & 2l —!

Electric current behaves in the same way, with current splitting and joining up just like water.

In the case of the circuit on the right the current flowing from the cell is 2 amps. When the current reaches the branch in the circuit, it splits into two equal parts of 1 amp. The currents then flow through the bulbs and join again to form a current of 2 amps.

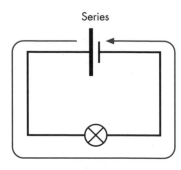

Series

Current flows along one route only.

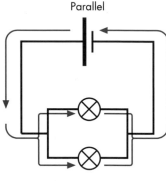

Parallel

Current splits and then joins together again.

2 litres in
2 litres out

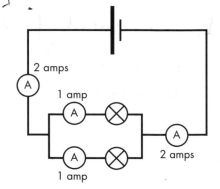

−1 litre → 2 litres out

2 litres in −1 litre →

2 amps
1 amp
A
A
A
A
2 amps
1 amp

What happens in parallel circuits?

To understand the brightness of the bulbs, we need to return to our ideas about resistance.

Imagine a water pump pushing water as hard as it can in a water system like the one on the right. It is more difficult for water to flow through the thin section of pipe than the wide sections. This means that the thin pipe has more resistance to the water than the wider ones. If a second thin pipe is added in parallel with the first, the total flow of water increases because the water can now flow through *both* thin pipes.

In an electrical circuit the same sort of thing happens.

A second bulb in parallel with the first glows just as brightly as when there is only one bulb, because the flow through each bulb is the same, but the total current is doubled.

The second bulb makes it easier for electric current to flow back to the cell so the total resistance in the circuit is less, and the total current is more.

ⓐ What would happen to the current if you had three bulbs in parallel?

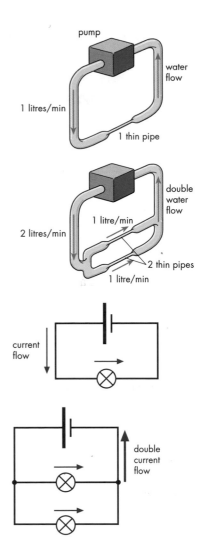

Do models always work?

The difficulty with any model in science is that it is never perfect. For instance, the water model doesn't explain what happens when a wire breaks. The water model would have electricity leaking out onto the floor. It is important to know when the model you are using breaks down.

ⓑ Think up your own model, perhaps using ants underground in tunnels, gerbils in tubes, blood in your body or cars on a motorway.

ⓒ Say how your model is like electricity.

ⓓ What are the limitations of your model?

QUESTIONS

1 Copy out the circuits on the right and label them series or parallel.

2 Write a sentence describing the flow of current in each of the circuits in question 1.

3 What effect will putting extra bulbs in parallel have on a cell? Try to use the words 'energy' and 'current' in your answer.

J6 ELECTRICITY AT HOME

TOPIC CHECKLIST

- What is a ring main?
- How do fuses work?
- Why is electricity dangerous to humans?
- Electricity in history

What is a ring main?

In houses the most common type of circuit is a **ring main**. It has this name because it forms a complete ring or loop inside the house. It is really a parallel circuit and has all of the advantages of a parallel circuit. Lights and sockets can be turned on and off independently and one blown bulb or a broken toaster doesn't stop the whole lot from working.

Switches at home

When you press a switch to turn on a light at home, you are connecting two parts of a ring main together through a bulb. Because the bulbs are in parallel, each bulb can be switched off separately.

Christmas lights

Many sets of Christmas lights are wired in series, so that if one bulb is taken out or blows, the whole lot stops working. The advantage of using a series circuit is that a lower current flows through it and so there is less danger of electrocution. However, care should still be taken when using Christmas lights.

How do fuses work?

A **fuse** is a safety device. It stops current flowing if the current gets too high. This is a good idea for three reasons:

- too high a current may damage components, so a cheap fuse blowing can save a lot of money.

- very high currents can cause fires. A fuse can help stop a house burning down and people dying.

- a fuse can stop current flowing if an electrical appliance has a fault. This can help to stop you getting an electric shock.

A fuse is simply a thin piece of wire designed to get hot and melt if too much current flows through it. Electrical energy is transformed into heat, which melts the fuse wire.

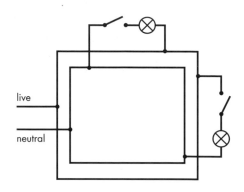

live

neutral

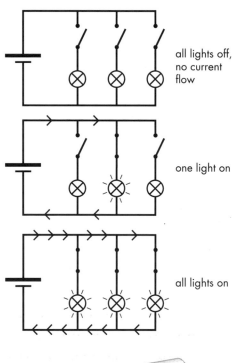

all lights off, no current flow

one light on

all lights on

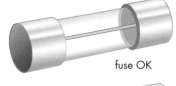

fuse OK

fuse melted

Why is electricity dangerous to humans?

All of the muscles in your body are controlled using tiny electric currents. You feel, see, hear, touch, smell and think using electricity. The nerves in your body use tiny electric currents to send signals to all parts of your body. Your heart beats because a regular jolt of electricity tells it to. Some people are kept alive by having a pacemaker which sends a pulse of electric current to the heart artificially.

ⓐ Why would a pacemaker need a battery that lasts a long time?

Unfortunately just as you would quickly die without electric current in your body, too much electric current can kill. If a tiny electric current makes your heart beat, imagine what a current a thousand times bigger will do! Touching high voltage equipment such as overhead power lines can easily kill, and people have died when their kites or fishing rods have touched power lines.

A heart pacemaker

Smaller electric currents can give you a nasty jolt but won't kill you, for example, those used in electric fences on farms.

Electricity in history

For centuries people have been interested in electricity. Towards the end of the 18th century an Italian physicist, Galvani, made frog's legs move by passing a current through them. Soon afterwards, another Italian professor, Volta, made the first electric battery. Watching scientists create electric effects, which seemed like magic, became a fashionable entertainment in nineteenth century London.

ⓑ The amount of push a cell has is called its voltage. Where did this name come from?

It wasn't until the late 19th century that our knowledge of electricity really developed and people began to put it to use.

ⓒ Other famous scientists include Benjamin Franklin, Charles Coulomb and Hans Oersted. When did they live and what discoveries did they make?

QUESTIONS

1 What is the advantage of using a ring main in a house for lighting?

2 Explain what happens when a fuse blows.

3 What is the danger in flying a kite?

4 What happens to the current flowing in the ring main as more bulbs are turned on at night?

K Forces and their effects

K1 WHERE DO WE COME ACROSS FORCES?

TOPIC CHECKLIST

- What are forces?
- How do we measure friction and weight?
- What is the difference between mass and weight?

What are forces?

Forces move things or stop them moving, change the shape of things or keep them the same shape.

Weight

Weight is the force that we all know most about. It is what keeps us on the ground or makes us fall down. A force meter can be used to measure weight.

Friction

Friction is the force you feel working against you when you push something across a surface. It occurs when two surfaces rub against each other. A lubricant like oil can reduce friction by keeping the surfaces apart.

Smoother surfaces tend to have less friction than rough ones, but friction forces also depend on how hard two surfaces are pushed together. It is quite easy to drag a rug across the floor, but much harder if someone is sitting on it.

ⓐ **Look at the picture. Ice moves much more easily across a surface than wood. Why?**

Friction is also the force that keeps your shoelaces tied and the sewing in your clothes. Fabric and thread have rough surfaces and the friction between them keeps them in place.

ⓑ **If you try tying a knot in plastic you will find that it often slithers undone. Why?**

Air can also drag on things with a type of force called **air resistance**. Things with large, square surfaces tend to meet more resistance from air than objects with smaller rounded surfaces. This is why a crumpled up piece of paper falls through the air more quickly than a flat sheet.

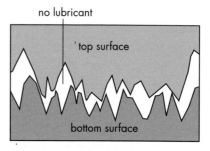

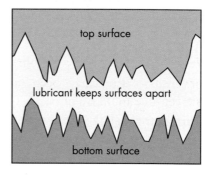

It is easier to push ice than wood.

120

Magnets

Magnets have a special type of force called **magnetic attraction**. They pull some types of metal to them (they **attract** them). Magnets together sometimes attract each other and sometimes push each other away.

How do we measure friction and weight?

Friction and weight can be measured using a spring balance, which is sometimes called a Newton meter. As the weight or force of friction gets larger, the spring stretches. The pointer on the end of the spring shows the size of the force.

What is the difference between mass and weight?

An ordinary house brick has an amount of 'stuff' in it. Just how much stuff is called its **mass**. The amount of mass depends on two things:

● How much material there is.

● What sort of material it is.

Mass is measured in kilograms (kg)

The brick is pulled down towards the Earth the whole time by the Earth's **gravity**. Its weight is its mass multiplied by the pull of gravity.

Weight is a force and is measured in newtons (N)

To work out the weight of an object on the Earth, multiply its mass in kg by 10.

Weight is a force; mass is the amount of 'stuff'.

Measuring friction using a Newton meter

> *Example*
>
> A giant lop eared rabbit has a mass of 15 kg. Its weight is 150 N.
>
> $$\text{Mass} \times 10 = \text{Weight}$$
> $$15 \times 10 \quad = 150\,\text{N}$$
>
> Be careful: to find weight in newtons you always have to use the mass in kilograms.

Weighing with a Newton meter

QUESTIONS

1 Newtons is the unit used to measure weight, what is the unit for mass?

2 Why is it harder to pull a sledge on grass than on snow?

3 How can you reduce friction between two surfaces?

4 What would be the mass of a dog if its weight was 560 N?

5 What would be the weight of a rat with a mass of 100 g? (Warning – the answer is not 1000 newtons)

WHY DO THINGS FLOAT?

TOPIC CHECKLIST

- Why do some things float?
- How do you measure upthrust?
- Why do some things sink?
- What is density?
- How do you calculate density?

Why do some things float?

If you float a piece of polystyrene in water, and then push it under the water, you can feel it pushing up against your hand. This force is called **upthrust**.

The force you feel as the polystyrene tries to float is the upthrust.

If you let go of the polystyrene when it is still underwater, it is pushed up to the surface by the upthrust.

How does upthrust happen? When you push the polystyrene under water, the level of the water rises. This is because the polystyrene has pushed the water out of the way. This is called **displacement**.

The water is being pulled down by gravity the whole time. When you let go of the polystyrene, the water is pulled down more than the polystyrene and pushes the polystyrene up.

If you look closely at a tennis ball floating in water, you will see that part of it is above the water and part of it below. The tennis ball sinks into the water until the upthrust from the displaced water is the same as the weight of the tennis ball. The two forces balance!

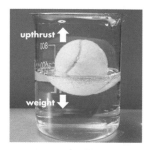

The weight of the ball and its upthrust balance

How do you measure upthrust?

Upthrust can be measured using a force meter. Hang an object on a force meter and note the size of the force (its weight). Now lower the mass into water – the reading on the force meter reduces. The amount the force reduces is the upthrust.

An object floating on the top of the water appears to have no weight.

a A plastic duck of mass 100 grams floats on the water. What is the weight of the duck?

b What is the size of the upthrust force on the duck?

Why do some things sink?

K

If you drop a potato in a bowl of water, it will sink. The weight of the potato is greater than the upthrust of the water and so the water cannot support it.

Sometimes you have two objects with the same weight, but one will float and one will sink. A gold ring will sink but a piece of balsa wood which is the same weight will float. Why?

The answer is that the important thing is **density**, not weight.

What is density?

Density is a measure of the amount of 'stuff' in a space. The more stuff that is packed into a space, the denser it is. Scientifically speaking, the stuff is called mass and the space is called volume. So the density of a material is the amount of mass in a volume.

The three blocks in the photograph have the same volume, but because they are made from different materials, they have different masses and different densities.

Metal, wood, polystyrene – same volume, different mass

In a similar way, if we look at three objects that all have the same mass but are made of different materials, the material with the biggest density takes up the least room.

Water has density too. To float, an object has to have a lower density than water. Anything which has a higher density will sink.

c Will a kilogram of feathers and a kilogram of concrete have the same mass?

d Will a kilogram of feathers and a kilogram of concrete take up the same space?

How do you calculate density?

To work out the density of a material, get a block of the material and find the mass of it using scales. Then measure the volume of the block. Now divide the mass of the block by the volume. Be careful to use the correct units, grams for mass, and centimetres cubed for volume.

> *Example*
>
> mass $= 8.9\,g$
>
> volume $= 1\,cm^3$
>
> density $=$ mass $\div$ volume
>
> density $= 8.9 \div 1$
> $\qquad\quad = 8.9\,g/cm^3$

Brass, water, wood – each has a mass of 10 g.

QUESTIONS

1 Describe the meanings of the words *volume* and *mass*.

2 What is the name of the force that pushes upwards on an object in water?

3 What happens to an object in water, if the weight of the object is greater than the upward force?

4 Calculate the density of a material which has a volume of 5 cm³ and a mass of 10 grams.

5 Why will gold sink in water?

Forces and their effects

Upthrust in other liquids

The size of the upthrust force on an object in a liquid, depends on two things:

● The volume of the object.

● The density of the liquid.

If an object is completely under water, the volume of liquid displaced is the same as the volume of the object. If the liquid is more dense than the object, the displaced liquid will weigh more and so be able to push the object upwards.

Water level rises

ⓐ **What happens if the object is more dense than the liquid?**

If a large object is put in water, it will displace more water than a small object, and the upthrust will be bigger. But whether it floats or sinks still depends on its density and the density of the water.

ⓑ **If all the steel from a ship was made into one block and dropped into the sea it would sink. But a ship floats. Why?**

If an object is placed in a denser liquid, the upthrust will be more because the weight of liquid displaced is more. For example if you swim in seawater, you will float higher in the water than in a swimming pool, because seawater is denser than fresh water.

Airship full of helium

Upthrust in air

Upthrust also works in air, but usually the upthrust force is so small that we don't notice it. If a large enough space is taken up by a light enough material, then it will float in air. A helium balloon is less dense than air and the sight of an airship floating above us is proof that floating in air is possible.

Hot air is less dense than cold air so it too floats. This is how heat moves around a room from a radiator, and hot air balloons fly.

Hot air balloon

Archimedes

The idea of displacement was first found by a Greek scientist, called Archimedes, who lived over 2000 years ago.

The story goes that the King set him a problem. He had given the royal jewellers some gold to make jewellery. He suspected that they were adding other metals to it and keeping the leftover gold. The jewellery weighed the same as the original lump of gold but they could have added some lower density metal.

The idea that gold and other metals had different densities was well known, but because jewellery is irregular in shape, there was no known way of working out its volume and so its density.

The solution came to Archimedes one day when he got into his bath. The bath was very full and when he got in, some of the water was pushed out. The deeper he sank in the more water came out.

Archimedes jumped out of the bath shouting 'eureka', which means 'I have found it'. What he had found was that:

whatever the volume of the object you put into a bath, the same volume of water would be displaced.

If you measure the volume of the displaced water, you have found the volume of the object, no matter what its shape.

Archimedes immersed a lump of gold, which was the same weight as the gold given to the jewellers, and measured the volume of water it displaced. Then he immersed the jewellery and found that the volume of water was different. The jewellers had cheated the king.

We still use this method of measuring the volume of irregularly shaped objects.

A common piece of equipment is the *eureka beaker*. This is a can with a spout sticking out of one side. When it is filled with water the can overflows through the spout. When the spout stops overflowing, the can is full. If an object is placed carefully in the can the water that is displaced overflows out of the spout and its volume can be measured.

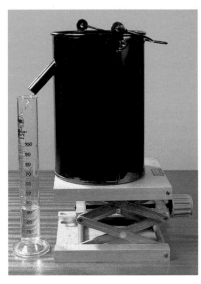

Eureka beaker

QUESTIONS

1 Which of the following materials will float in water: copper, ice, wood, steel?

2 Why must a eureka beaker be full of water before it is used?

3 Describe how you can measure the volume of a stone.

4 Explain why a swimmer will find it easier to float in the sea than in a river.

5 Explain how Archimedes could use his discovery to check the gold in jewellery.

HOW DO FORCES BALANCE?

TOPIC CHECKLIST

- What happens when forces are balanced?
- What happens when forces are not balanced?
- How do we show forces in diagrams?

What happens when forces are balanced?

Forces are balanced when two or more forces cancel each other out. Forces are always balanced when an object stays still, but an object moving at a constant speed in a straight line also has balanced forces.

Keeping still

The trampolinist in the photograph is just preparing to start a routine. She is still, so we know that any forces acting on her are balanced. Her weight is acting downwards, so where is the force coming from to balance her weight?

The answer is the reaction force of the trampoline surface. The springs around the trampoline stretch until the weight of the person is balanced by the upward force of the trampoline. If a lighter person gets onto the trampoline, the springs do not stretch as much before they balance the weight of the lighter person.

What about the cat sitting on the table? The cat has weight, so the table must be pushing upwards. The legs of the table have actually been squashed a tiny fraction of a millimetre and are pushing back against the weight of the cat, like very stiff springs.

It is not just force and reaction force which stop things moving. Sometimes forces can be pulling against each other in opposite directions and this means that the object in the middle does not move.

In the tug of war, the two teams are pulling against each other with the same force, so they stay where they are.

Keeping a steady speed

When forces are balanced, the object is not necessarily still. It can be moving, but when the forces are balanced it will move at exactly the same speed all the time.

A cyclist on a straight road will move at a constant speed as long as the force of her legs on the pedals balances the air resistance and friction from the road which are reacting against her pedalling force.

What happens when forces are not balanced?

The photographs show people in situations where the forces on them are not balanced. In each situation the person or object will either stop moving or start to move.

For example, the bunjee jumper is getting to the bottom of the fall. The bunjee is pulling upwards with a force greater than his weight, so he will slow down, stop and then start to move back upwards.

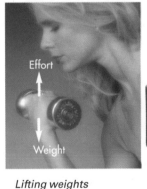

ⓐ **Describe the effect of the unbalanced forces in the photograph of the athlete.**

How do we show forces in diagrams?

To help us show the forces in situations, we use force arrows. The bigger the force, the longer the arrow. So small forces are shown using short arrows.

If the weight is not moving, its weight must be balanced by the force of the arm muscles pushing up. This is a reaction force.

Lifting weights

QUESTIONS

1 What can you say about the forces on a brick lying still on the floor?

2 Draw a diagram showing the forces on a boat floating on the sea.

3 What would happen to the forces in the springs in a chair if a heavy person sat in it?

4 Draw the force arrows for a car accelerating away from some traffic lights.

What factors affect friction?

Friction is a reaction force; this means that it always pushes in the opposite direction to the force moving something or trying to move it. Friction is usually caused by surfaces rubbing together.

We make friction less by making the surfaces smoother, or using **lubrication**.

A lubricant such as oil flows in between surfaces and fills the bumps and hollows. This keeps the surfaces apart so they behave as if they were smooth. Graphite and grease can also be used as lubricants.

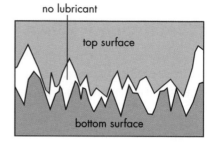

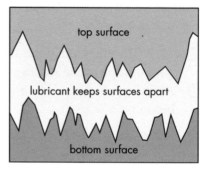

How is friction useful?

Without friction life would be very difficult.

A car uses friction to move forward. If there were no friction between the tyres and the road, the wheels would spin but the car would stay still.

When the brakes are applied, the friction between the tyres and the road slows the car down.

Sometimes the friction between the tyres and the road becomes very small, when it is wet or icy. Water on the road acts like a lubricant, and ice has a very smooth surface.

How do we measure speed?

Speed is a measurement of how fast you are moving. We measure it by how far you travel in a certain time.

In the UK we measure speed in miles per hour. For example, if you are travelling at 50 miles per hour in a car, you will travel 50 miles in one hour if you carry on at that speed for the whole hour. Elsewhere people use kilometres per hour.

In science experiments we measure speed in metres per second, which means, how many metres are moved in one second.

For example if a sledge slides 20 metres in 2 seconds, how fast is it travelling? To find how far it moves in one second we divide the 20 metres by two. This tells us that it moved 10 metres in one second (10 m/s).

You can see from this that

$$\text{speed} = \frac{\text{distance}}{\text{time}}$$

$$\text{speed} = \frac{20}{2}$$

$$\text{speed} = 10 \text{ m/s}$$

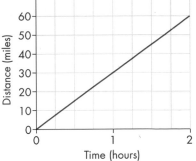

ⓐ If a pupil runs 100 metres in 20 seconds, how far will they run in one second?

60 miles in 2 hours is 30 miles per hour

We can show speed in a graph. The graph above shows a bus moving at a steady 30 miles per hour. Notice the line of the graph is straight, this means steady speed on this graph.

The next graph shows the journey of a bus as it travels between towns. Try to describe what you think is happening at each section of the graph. For example, in the first section it is travelling at a steady speed.

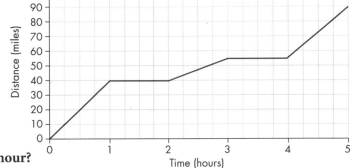

ⓑ At which places on the bus graph is the bus not moving?

ⓒ How far has the bus travelled after one hour?

ⓓ How far does the bus travel in the third hour?

ⓔ What is the total distance travelled by the bus?

ⓕ How long does the bus take to travel this distance?

How long does it take to stop?

The faster a car is moving the longer it takes to stop. Put another way, the higher your speed the bigger the distance you need to stop.

The Highway Code has a list of braking distances for cars travelling at different speeds. Plot a graph of the braking distances from the Highway Code information on the right. Plot speed along the *x*-axis and braking distance along the *y*-axis.

Braking distance

Speed (mph)	20	30	40	50	60	70
Braking distance (metres)	6	14	24	38	55	75

QUESTIONS

1 Why do we put grit on icy roads in winter?

2 The tread on car tyres moves water from between the tyre and the road. Why is this important?

3 Sometimes brakes squeak. Why should you not oil them?

4 Estimate the braking distance of a car travelling at 35mph.

How much does a spring stretch?

All materials stretch when pulled, but some stretch less than others.

Springs are designed to stretch and then go back to their original length when the force is removed. We can predict exactly how much they stretch with different amounts of force.

The **extension** of a spring is its length when stretched minus its original length.

Hang a spring from a hook and make a note of its length.

Hang a series of masses on the spring and measure the length of the spring each time.

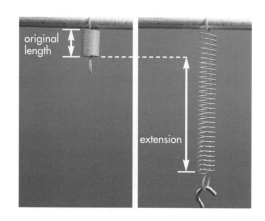

Using the results on the right, plot a graph of the mass on the spring against the extension of the spring.

a What type of line joins the points on the graph?

b When 100 grams is on the spring the length has increased by 34 mm, if another 100 grams is hung on the spring, what is the increase of length this time?

c What is the pattern in these results?

Results for spring stretching experiment	
Mass applied (g)	Extension (mm)
0	0
20	7
40	15
60	22
80	28
100	34
120	41
140	50
160	57
180	62
200	72
220	80
240	90
260	95

If the same experiment is tried using an elastic band rather than a spring, the results look different. The graph on the right shows the results using an elastic band.

ⓓ **Describe the difference between the graph for an elastic band and a spring.**

Extension of rubber band with force applied

Investigating friction

Use a block of wood that has different measurements for length, width and thickness. Attach a hook in the centre of one end so that a Newton meter can be hooked to it. Measure the friction needed to just get the block to move by pulling the block with the Newton meter.

Predict what would happen to the friction if you changed the following:

● The area of the surface the block rests on.

● The surface the block rests on

● The weight on top of the block

You could also try putting a little sand between the block and the surface. Investigate using different depths of sand.

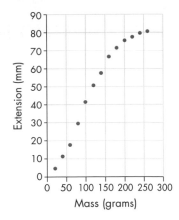

Presenting experimental data

In an experiment on friction, a pupil investigated the weights on a block and the force needed to just get it to move. The data is shown in the table on the right.

Plot a graph of the data with weights along the X axis (bottom of the graph) and friction force on the Y axis (up the side of the graph).

ⓔ **Describe the relationship of friction to weight on the block.**

ⓕ **The data does not lie exactly on a straight line, why is this?**

ⓖ **What variables will have been controlled in this experiment to ensure a fair test?**

Weight (N)	Friction force (N)
0	15
1	17
2	20
3	21
4	24
5	25

QUESTIONS

1 Tarmac is a more expensive road surface than concrete, so why is it used?

L The solar system and beyond

WHERE AND WHAT IS THE EARTH?

What is the Earth?

When the Earth is seen from space it is the shape of a slightly flattened ball. But when we look at it from ground level it looks flat. The reason for this difference in appearance is because the Earth is so big that you cannot see its curve when you are standing on it.

The Earth moves around the Sun in a nearly perfect circle. This is called its **orbit**. As it moves around the Sun the Earth is spinning around. The Sun provides all the light for the Earth.

How does the Earth spin?

The Earth is like an apple spinning on a rod pushed through its centre. The rod is held at an angle.

The Earth does not have a real rod through its centre but an imaginary one which runs through from the **North Pole** to the **South Pole**. This is called the Earth's **axis**.

The **equator** is an imaginary ring around the widest point of the ball. It runs around the middle of the Earth.

The **Northern Hemisphere** is the half of the Earth closest to the North Pole.

The **Southern Hemisphere** is the half closest to the South Pole.

The Earth

The Earth looks flat from ground level.

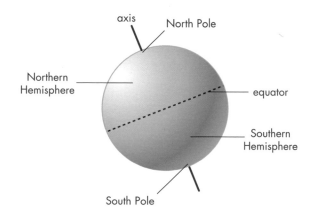

Why is there day and night?

Day is when your bit of the Earth is facing the Sun. Night is when Earth has spun around so that your bit is facing away from the Sun. It is always daytime somewhere on the Earth and always night somewhere, depending on which parts are facing the Sun and which are not.

The Earth is spinning just like a ball and so places on the Earth's surface move from night into day every time the Earth spins once. The Earth takes 24 hours (1 day) to spin once.

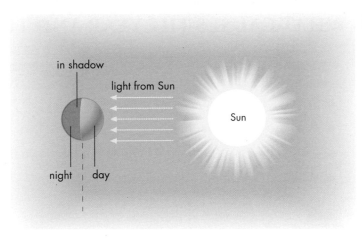

Why does the Sun seem to move across the sky?

It looks as if the Sun moves across the sky. We talk about sunrise when we see it rise above the horizon and sunset when it sinks down behind it at the end of the day. But sunrise is actually the bit of the Earth we are standing on spinning gradually around into the Sun's light and sunset is when our bit of Earth is spinning gradually out of the sunlight again.

Time around the world

To help make sense of when the Sun rises and sets at different places around the Earth, people have divided the Earth into **time zones**. There are 24 time zones around the world; generally each one is one hour different from the next. In Great Britain just one time zone is used, and all the clocks read the same time throughout the country. America, however, is so big that it has six different time zones. In a time zone, **noon** is roughly when the Sun is at its highest.

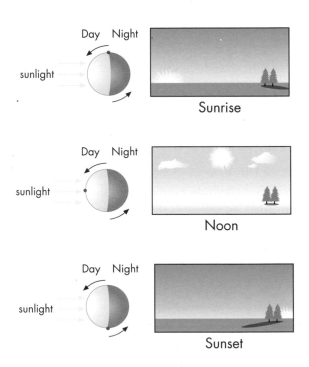

Sunrise

Noon

Sunset

QUESTIONS

1. Draw a diagram of the Earth showing the equator, the North and South Poles.

2. What time would it be if the Sun was directly above you?

3. How many times will the Earth spin in a week?

4. How much of the Earth's surface is lit by the Sun at any time?

5. The Earth is spinning a little slower every year. What effect will this have on the length of the day?

6. Why is it that ships disappear over the horizon?

7. Explain why clocks set on the east coast of the USA show a different time from those on the west coast.

WHAT CAUSES THE YEAR AND THE SEASONS?

TOPIC CHECKLIST

- So what is a year?
- Why are there seasons?
- Why is the Sun at different heights during the year?
- Why is it warmer in summer than winter?

So what is a year?

The Earth is spinning around its axis but also moving in a circle around the Sun. A year is the time it takes for the Earth to go round the Sun once, about $365\frac{1}{4}$ days.

Our calendars do not have quarter days so once every 4 years we have a 366-day year to bring our calendars back in line with the movement of the Earth around the Sun. This is called a leap year.

Why are there seasons?

In the UK there are distinct seasons in the year. Summer is warm with long days and short nights; winter is cold with short days and long nights; spring and autumn are in between.

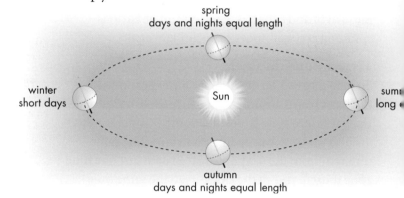

The seasons are caused by the tilt of the Earth on its axis. Look at the views of the Earth above. You can see that, in winter, the tilt of the Earth makes the UK pass more quickly through the Sun's light than in summer, when the tilt of the Earth makes the days longer.

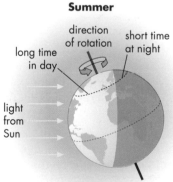

In summer the axis of the Earth is tilted towards the Sun, so days are longer in the Northern Hemisphere.

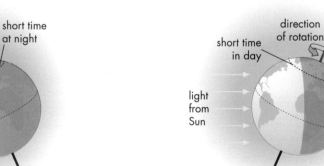

In winter the axis of the Earth is tilted away from the Sun, so days are shorter in the Northern Hemisphere.

At the poles of the Earth there is constant daylight in summer and constant night in winter.

(a) Look at the diagram of the Earth's orbit around the Sun in a year. Why is there constant light at the North Pole in summer and constant dark in winter?

(b) Why does Australia have a summer when we have a winter?

Why is the Sun at different heights during the year?

In the UK in the summer, we see the Sun high in the sky at noon. In winter the Sun seems much lower in the sky at noon. This is because of the different angle of the Earth to the Sun.

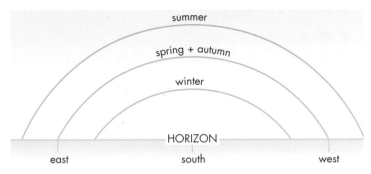

The Sun rises higher in the sky in summer.

Why is it warmer in summer than winter?

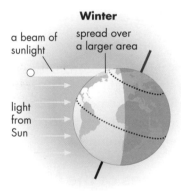

(a) As the Earth tilts towards the Sun, the noonday sun is spread over a fairly small area, so the Sun's energy hitting the Earth is more intense. This makes the days hotter.

(b) As the Earth tilts away from the Sun, the noonday sun is spread over a large area, so the Sun's energy hitting the Earth is less intense. This makes the days colder.

The different angle of the Earth to the Sun changes the amount of energy arriving at the Earth's surface from the Sun. During summertime in the UK, the Sun is more or less directly above us at noon. A beam of sunlight hitting the ground is fairly intense and warms us quite a lot. In winter, a beam of sunlight hits the Earth at an angle and is spread over a larger area. The light is less intense, so warms us less.

QUESTIONS

1 Why are the lengths of Earth days in spring and autumn the same?

2 The Earth is tilted at about 23 degrees. What would be the effect on the seasons if the tilt was 45 degrees?

3 The Arctic circle is the area of the Earth that gets at least one day in the year when the Sun does not set. If the Sun does not set here, why is it so cold?

L3   WHERE DOES THE MOON FIT IN?

TOPIC CHECKLIST

- How do we see the Sun and the Moon?
- What are the phases of the Moon?
- What is a solar eclipse?
- What is a lunar eclipse?

Our Earth has a smaller rocky body orbiting it just as the Earth itself orbits the Sun. This is called the Moon.

The Moon takes about 28 days to orbit the Earth. A month is roughly the time it takes the Moon to orbit the Earth. The Moon also spins on its axis about once every 28 Earth days.

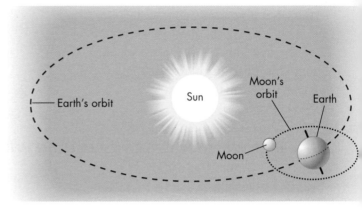

How do we see the Sun and the Moon?

We see the Sun because it creates its own light. The Moon does not create its own light. We see it because it reflects the Sun's light. When something creates its own light we call it **luminous**. Objects which do not create their own light are **non-luminous**.

What are the phases of the Moon?

Because the Moon is orbiting the Earth, the amount of the Moon that reflects light towards the Earth changes, and this makes the **phases of the Moon**.

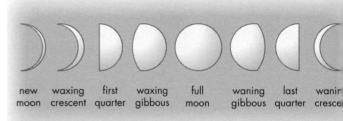

| new moon | waxing crescent | first quarter | waxing gibbous | full moon | waning gibbous | last quarter | waning crescent |

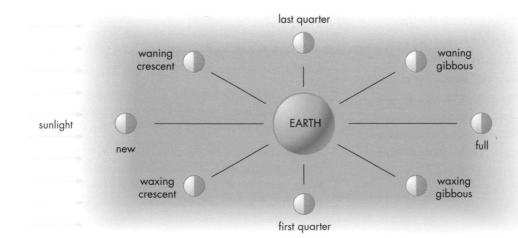

What is a solar eclipse?

A solar **eclipse** happens when the Sun, Moon and Earth line up with the Moon in the middle. Although the Sun is much bigger than the Moon it is also much further away from the Earth so it looks the same size as the Moon. This is why when they line up the Moon can completely cover the Sun for a couple of minutes.

A solar eclipse does not block out the Sun all over the world, just in certain places. A total solar eclipse was visible from this country in 1999. The next one visible from the UK will be in 2090.

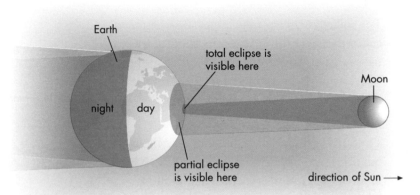

Moon's shadow during a total eclipse

A total solar eclipse has four main stages

The Moon starts to cover the sun

The start of totality where the Moon first totally covers the Sun

The end of totality where the Moon stops covering the Sun

The eclipse finishes

What is a lunar eclipse?

A lunar eclipse happens when the Moon passes through the Earth's shadow, that is, when the Earth is lined up between the Moon and the Sun and blocks the Sun's light from the Moon. Again this is fairly rare. A total lunar eclipse can last for two hours because the Earth casts a bigger shadow than the Moon.

Scientists can gain a great deal of evidence from eclipses which helps them to calculate distances of planets and stars from the Earth and find information about solar flares which affect our weather.

QUESTIONS

1 How long would days and nights on the Moon be?

2 The Moon is non-luminous. How do we see it?

3 Explain what is happening when we see a new moon and a full moon.

4 A solar eclipse is the Moon's shadow falling on the Earth. Explain how this happens.

5 Draw a diagram showing how a lunar eclipse happens.

WHAT DOES THE SOLAR SYSTEM CONSIST OF?

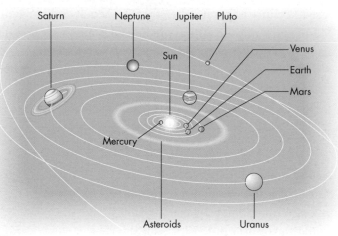

TOPIC CHECKLIST

- What is in the solar system?
- What are the distances involved?

What is in the solar system?

The solar system has nine large balls of material called **planets** orbiting the Sun; some of these have large bodies orbiting them called **moons**. There are also thousands of smaller lumps of rock called **asteroids** in a belt between the fourth and fifth planets.

There are nine planets of different sizes orbiting the Sun.

The Sun is a huge ball of glowing gas, which gives out immense amounts of light and heat. It has a diameter of around one and a half million kilometres (110 times bigger than the Earth).

The next diagram shows the relative sizes of the planets in order from the Sun.

All of these planets orbit the Sun in a similar way to the Earth. Pluto is a little odd because its orbit is at an angle to the orbits of the other planets and instead of being nearly circular, it is roughly egg shaped or elliptical.

What are the distances involved?

To understand the distance of the Sun from the Earth, it helps to think of the Sun as the size of a grapefruit and the Earth as a grain of sugar. This is how big they are compared to each other.

On this scale the grain of sugar would be the length of a swimming pool away from the grapefruit. Pluto, the furthest planet from the Sun, would be one kilometre away from the grapefruit and little bigger than a piece of dust.

QUESTIONS

1 Which is the biggest planet?

2 How long does it take Jupiter and Mercury to orbit the Sun?

3 How long does it take Venus and Saturn to turn around their axis?

4 Which planet has the most moons?

5 Draw up a table to show the distance of the planets from the Sun with the time it takes them to orbit. What is the relationship between them?

Neptune
Distance from Sun 4 498 000 000 km
Diameter 49 532 km
rotation about axis 16 hours
Length of year 60 193 Earth days
Moons 8 known
Mass 17.2 times Earth

Uranus
Distance from Sun 2 871 000 000 km
Diameter 51 118 km
rotation about axis 17 hours
Length of year 30 681 Earth days
Moons 17 known
Mass 14.5 times Earth

Pluto
Distance from Sun 5 900 000 000 km
Diameter 2 274 km
rotation about axis 6 Earth days
Length of year 90 465 Earth days
Moons 1
Mass 0.002 times Earth

Saturn
Distance from Sun 1427 000 000 km
Diameter 120 000 km
rotation about axis 11 hours
Length of year 10 760 Earth days
Moons 18 known
Mass 95 times Earth

Jupiter
Distance from Sun 778 400 000 km
Diameter 140 000 km
rotation about axis 10 hours
Length of year 4336 Earth days
Moons 16
Mass 318 times Earth

Mercury
Distance from Sun 57 900 000 km
Diameter 4 880 km
rotation about axis 59 Earth days
Length of year 88 Earth days
Moons 0
Mass 0.06 times Earth

Venus
Distance from Sun 108 200 000 km
Diameter 12 104 km
rotation about axis 243 Earth days
Length of year 225 Earth days
Moons 0
Mass 0.82 times Earth

Earth
Distance from Sun 149 600 000 km
Diameter 12 756 km
rotation about axis 24 hours
Length of year 365.25 days
Moons 1

Mars
Distance from Sun 227 900 000 km
Diameter 6 794 km
rotation about axis 25 hours
Length of year 687 Earth days
Moons 2
Mass 0.11 times Earth

The solar system and beyond

L5 STARS

TOPIC CHECKLIST

- Where are the stars?
- Why can't you see stars during the day?
- How do we use the stars?
- Movement of the stars

Where are the stars?

Stars come in a variety of sizes from supergiants, which are 300 times the size of the Sun, to neutron stars about the size of the Earth. They also vary greatly in brightness and colour. A dim star that is quite close, can look similar to a very bright star much further away.

The brightest stars are 100 000 times brighter than our Sun and the dimmest are 100 000 times less bright.

To measure the distances between the stars it is useful to use a unit which is very large. It is common to use the distance travelled by light in a certain time. In a year, light will travel 9 461 000 000 000 km. This distance is called a **light year**.

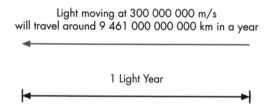

Light moving at 300 000 000 m/s
will travel around 9 461 000 000 000 km in a year

1 Light Year

The closest star is 4.2 light years away and the furthest stars discovered are 10 billion light years away. Because even the closest star is a very long way away, all stars look like points of light.

Why can't you see stars during the day?

Stars are actually very faint lights because they are so very far away. During the day, the light from our nearest star, the Sun, is so powerful that we cannot see the faint lights of the stars.

Even at night, the light of towns and cities makes it difficult to see some fainter stars. Telescopes on the surface of the Earth are limited by the air that they look through. Telescopes in space can pick up light from much further away than Earth based devices.

How do we use the stars?

The stars always have the same pattern in the sky and this can be useful for us. For example, before compasses were invented, sailors used to find their way using the stars. The Pole Star always appears above the North Pole. By finding the Pole Star in the sky you can tell which way is north. Of course, this is not much use when the sky is cloudy!

The patterns formed by stars have long ago been given names, like the bear, the swan, the lion, the hunter. These patterns are called constellations.

Movement of the stars

The Earth is spinning which means that the pattern of stars appears to move across the sky, in the same way as the Sun appears to move. The Pole Star is almost exactly in line with the axis of the Earth and so does not appear to move.

A camera was used to take several photographs of the night sky at intervals, without moving; this shows the apparent movement of the stars.

Although even the nearest stars are enormous distances away, planets have been discovered orbiting other stars. Exactly what these planets are like is still a mystery.

Star trails

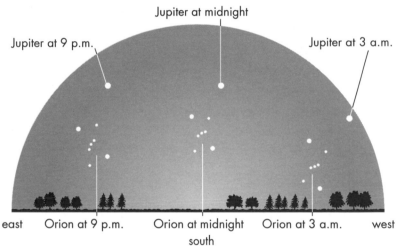

Follow the last two stars in the constellation 'The Plough' to find the Pole Star.

constellation Ursa Major (The Plough)

Pole star (Polaris)

Jupiter at midnight

Jupiter at 9 p.m.

Jupiter at 3 a.m.

east   Orion at 9 p.m.   Orion at midnight   Orion at 3 a.m.   west
south

QUESTIONS

1 Why are astronomical observatories built well away from towns and cities?

2 Light travels about 300 000 km each second. If it takes light about 8 minutes to get from the Sun to the Earth, how far is that in km?

3 What is a light second?

4 Why do people who live in Australia never see Polaris, the North Pole Star?

5 How many metres is one light minute?

IS THERE LIFE ANYWHERE ELSE?

TOPIC CHECKLIST

- What sort of planet can support life?
- Is there life elsewhere in our solar system?
- Was there life on Mars?
- Looking for life
- Are there any planets out there like the Earth?

Mercury 167°C
too hot

Venus 464°C
even hotter

Earth 15°C
just right

Mars –63°C
a bit too cold

Jupiter –110°C
too much pressure
and too cold

Saturn –140°C
too cold

Uranus –197°C
far too cold

Neptune –200°C
far too cold again

Pluto –223°C
you're joking!

What sort of planet can support life?

We know that the Earth has life on it, but does life exist on any other planet? There is an enormous variety of life on Earth, but all life on Earth has at least three common features:

- All need water.
- All get their energy either directly or indirectly from sunlight.
- All need carbon.

Earth is a nearly perfect environment for life to exist:

- The temperature of the Earth means that there is plenty of liquid water.
- There is a large amount of carbon.
- There is plenty of sunlight.

Is there life elsewhere in our solar system?

The obvious place to look for life similar to ours is on planets or moons with similar conditions to the Earth. So which of the planets are similar to Earth?

Mercury is just too hot being very close to the Sun and has almost no atmosphere and no water.

Venus is a very similar size to the Earth and so has an atmosphere, but is even hotter than Mercury because of its greenhouse effect.

The gas giants Jupiter, Saturn, Uranus and Neptune have no solid surface, and the gas is very cold indeed.

Pluto is not only very small but incredibly cold at around –200° C, a very unlikely place for life.

Of the major planets other than Earth, only Mars has even a remote chance of being able to support life, and even here it is very unlikely.

Was there life on Mars?

Mars is now a cold airless planet. It has water, but this is locked up as ice. The surface of Mars is covered with features that suggest that, many millions of years ago, the planet was warmer and liquid water flowed.

There were volcanoes and the planet was bombarded by meteorites. This kept the planet warmer than it would normally be, that far from the Sun. Life could have started back then but it is unlikely still to be there now.

Mars

Looking for life

It is difficult to tell from a distance whether there was, or is, any life on Mars. So we have sent missions to Mars to find out.

The Viking missions sent landers to the surface with complex experiments designed to look for signs of life. Nothing so far from the landers gives us any positive evidence that life does, or did, exist on Mars. The most positive evidence for life on Mars has actually been found on Earth.

A meteorite discovered in Antarctica was found to be made up of the same chemicals as Mars. It was probably hurled into space during a violent volcanic eruption, landing on the Earth 13 000 years ago. The meteorite contains chemicals with carbon in them, and tiny structures that could have been made by microscopic life. This evidence is very weak and may be nothing but coincidence.

Viking lander on Mars

Are there any planets out there like the Earth?

We don't know! It was only towards the end of the twentieth century that we became sure that there were any planets around other stars. The chance that any planet around any one sun is right for life is pretty low, but there are an awful lot of stars. Scientists disagree about the probability of life on other planets, and until we make contact with an extra-terrestrial, the argument will continue.

Is anybody there?

QUESTIONS

1 What conditions does life need?

2 Venus is very similar to the Earth in size, so why is it unlikely to support life?

3 Why is it unlikely that there is life on Mars now, even if there used to be?

4 What has happened to the water on Mars?

5 The Viking missions were unmanned. Why do you think this was so?

6 Why does the meteorite from Mars suggest that there may possibly have once been life on Mars?

WHAT IS BEYOND THE SOLAR SYSTEM?

Looking at the sky

Since prehistoric times, people have looked at the stars in the sky. When you look at something without a telescope or binoculars people say that you are using the **naked eye**.

For thousands of years people have been able to see the bright points of light in the sky they called stars. Using just your eyes there is a lot you can see, including thousands of stars, comets and the brightest planets.

Telescopes

In 1610 Galileo used one of the first telescopes to look at the skies. He found Saturn's rings, four moons orbiting Jupiter, craters on the Moon and he discovered that there were far more stars than anybody had realised.

The early telescopes used lenses made from glass to magnify light from distant stars and planets. To make more powerful telescopes the lenses had to be bigger, but large lenses are very heavy and difficult to make.

Another type of telescope, called a reflecting telescope, uses mirrors instead, and these can be much bigger. The bigger the telescope, the better you can see the star or planet. Sir Isaac Newton, who was famous for his work on gravity, built the first reflecting telescope in 1668.

Sir William Herschel and his sister Caroline were both astronomers and together they catalogued thousands of stars. William discovered the planet Uranus in 1781 using a telescope in his garden. He also built a large reflecting telescope, with which he was able to discover two moons of Uranus and more moons of Saturn. The mirror for this telescope was the biggest of its time and he built it in his kitchen.

An early observatory

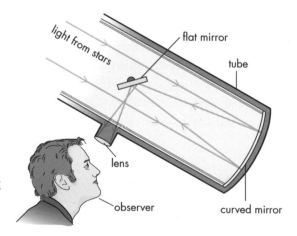

Reflecting telescope

Sometimes astronomers work out that things are there before they see them. Neptune is a very faint object when viewed from the Earth. It was only found because it pulls the orbit of Uranus a certain way so scientists knew that there was another planet there and knew where to look for it.

As science and technology have advanced, larger and larger telescopes have been built. The largest one is built in a natural mountain crater, is over 300 metres across and can receive radio waves coming from stars so far away we cannot pick up their light.

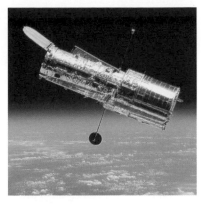
Hubble telescope

Telescopes on Earth all suffer from the fact that light from the stars has to pass through the air, which makes it more difficult to see them clearly. More recently the Hubble space telescope has been put into orbit around the Earth. Because there is no air in space, the Hubble telescope can produce images of more objects which are at greater distances.

Space exploration

Because stars are so far away and it takes even light over four years to arrive from the closest one, we have only been able to look at them, not send spacecraft to them. Our own solar system is a different matter.

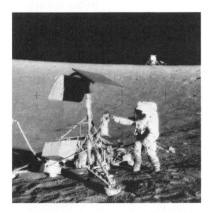
Moonlanding

The Moon is a relatively short hop away, less than 400 000 kilometres away. The first person to visit the moon, Neil Armstrong, stepped onto it in 1969, and from then on, we have been able to study the moon closely.

But the planets are so far away that only unmanned spacecraft have been sent there. Most of the planets have been visited by probes that have flown past and taken pictures or landed to measure wind speeds and examine the soil and atmosphere.

Saturn

QUESTIONS

1 Describe what Galileo and Herschel discovered and when and how they did it.

2 Why did the invention of a reflecting telescope help people to see more than a lens telescope?

3 Why can scientists see the universe more clearly with a space telescope than one on Earth?

4 Why are probes to the planets unmanned?

5 How was Neptune discovered?

6 The furthest planet discovered so far, Pluto, has a very strange orbit. This makes some scientists think that there may be a tenth planet. Why?

Glossary

acids   substances that react with **alkalis** and sometimes have a sour taste

adapted   when plants, animals or **cells** have special features which help them to survive or do their job

adolescence   the part of life between childhood and adulthood during which **puberty** happens

afterbirth   the name for the **placenta** when it passes out of the woman's body after birth

agar   a kind of jelly – not for eating!

air resistance   force acting against movement in air

alkalis   substances that react with **acids**

ammeter   a device for measuring electric **current**

amniotic fluid   the fluid surrounding and protecting the baby in the womb

ampere   unit of electric current

antacid   substance that uses up or cancels out an **acid**

anther   part of a flower which makes **pollen cells**

asteroids   small rocks that orbit the Sun usually between the orbits of Jupiter and Mars

atom   the smallest bit of something

attract   pull towards

axis   imaginary line the Earth rotates around

bacteria   tiny living things that can cause disease

battery   two or more **cells** in **series**

bicarbonate of soda   another name for sodium hydrogen carbonate

biomass   plants used as a **fuel**

birth   when the baby is pushed out of a woman's **uterus**

brine   salt solution

capital (resources)   energy resources that cannot be replaced

carnivore   an animal which eats only other animals

caustic   substance that can burn living tissue

cell division   the way in which new **cells** are made

cell membrane   holds the **cytoplasm** together and controls what goes into and out of the cell

cell wall   stops the cell changing shape, collapsing or bursting

cell (unit J)   a device that transforms chemical energy into electrical energy

cells (unit A)   the building blocks of animals and plants

cervix   the opening of the **uterus**

chemical change   a change which results in a new substance or substances

chlorine   a chemical that can kill **bacteria**

chlorophyll   the green substance found in plants that makes food

chloroplast   the place in the cells where **chlorophyll** is found

chromatogram   the 'colour picture' you get as the result of **chromatography**

chromatography   a method of separating a mixture of **solutes**

circuit   complete route from positive terminal of a **cell** or **battery** to the negative terminal

circuit diagram	number of **circuit symbols** representing an electrical **circuit**
classifying	putting living things into groups
combustible	can burn
component	part of an electric **circuit**
condense	change from a gas to a liquid
conductors	materials that allow heat or electricity to move through them easily
conserved	kept the same
consumer	animals which must eat other living things for food
contract, contractions	what the **uterus** muscles do when they push the baby out during **birth**
corrode	to eat away a substance
corrosive	can **corrode** something. On a Hazard label, this means "attacks and destroys living tissue, including eyes and skin"
cover slip	place this over your specimen when you examine it under the **microscope**
current	flow of charged particles
cytoplasm	the place where chemical reactions happen in a **cell**
density	a measure of how much **mass** is in a **volume**
detergent	a substance used for cleaning
develop	change physically and emotionally
diffusion	the spreading out movement of **particles**
displacement	the amount of liquid or gas moved out of the way by a solid floating or immersed in it

distillation	separating and collecting the **solvent** from a **mixture**
diurnal	an animal which is active during the day and sleeps at night
dormant structure	structures formed by animals and plants to survive harsh environmental conditions
eclipse	when the Moon casts a shadow on the Earth
egg cell	the female **gamete** in humans and plants
electric current	flow of **electrons**
electrons	charged particles that can move through **conductors**
element	simplest substance
embryo	bundle of cells resulting from **fertilisation,** before separate **organs** develop
energy	the ability to do work
energy source	anything that can give useful energy
environmental factors	the conditions in a **habitat** which affect what can survive there
environmental variation	features which have been affected by surroundings
epidermal tissue	the outer protective layer of **cells** on a leaf
epithelium cell	the outer protective layer of **cells** in animals
equator	imaginary line around the Earth half way between the **North and South Poles**
evaporate	change from a liquid to a gas
evidence	measurements or observations used to prove something
extension	how much longer a material becomes when stretched

external fertilisation	when **fertilisation** happens outside the female's body
extract	to get something out of something else
fertilisation	when the male and female **gametes** join together
fetus	a developing baby inside its mother's **uterus** whose **organs** are growing
filtering	method of separating solid bits from a liquid
fire triangle	a diagram used to show the three things a fire needs to burn
foam	a mixture of a gas and a liquid *or* a gas and a solid
focus	to make a **microscope** image more clear
food chain	a diagram showing what an animal eats and what eats it
food web	a diagram made of lots of joined up **food chains**, showing what eats what in a **habitat**
fossil fuel	**energy resource** made from the bodies of animals or plants that lived millions of years ago (coal, oil, gas)
friction	force acting against movement when two surfaces touch
fuel	substance that can be burnt releasing heat energy and is an **energy resource**
gamete	male and female sex **cells** (sperm cell and egg cell in humans; pollen cell and egg cell in plants)
gel	a mixture of a liquid and a solid
geothermal	energy transferred from heat inside the Earth
gestation period	the period during which a woman is **pregnant**
gills	a fish gets oxygen from the water through these
granite	a kind of rock

gravity	attraction of any **mass** to any other **mass**
grow	increase in size
growth	an increase in size
habitat	the place where an animal or plant lives
hard water	water that contains dissolved chemicals that stop **detergents** working properly and cause limescale in kettles
harmful	can make you ill if swallowed, breathed in or absorbed through the skin (Hazard label)
hazardous	has some risk connected with it
heart	the **organ** which pumps blood
hemisphere	half of a sphere (northern half of the Earth is northern hemisphere)
herbivore	an animal which eats only plants
hibernation	when an animal spends the winter asleep
hormones	control changes in the body like **ovulation** and **menstruation**
hydroelectric	transforming the energy from moving water into electrical energy
hydrogen	colourless gas that 'pops' with a lighted splint
identical twins	two children, born at the same time, which look exactly the same as each other
implant	when the **embryo** attaches itself to the **uterus** wall
impurities	unwanted substances mixed with the substance you want
indicator	a chemical that changes colour in **acids** and **alkalis**
inherited	passed on from one generation to the next
inherited variation	those of your features which were passed on to you by your parents
insecticide	a substance that kills insects

insoluble	a substance that won't dissolve in a **solvent**	**maturation**	when an **egg cell** ripens inside an **ovary**
intensity (light)	the strength of light	**menstrual cycle**	the monthly cycle of changes in the female **reproductive organs**
internal fertilisation	when **fertilisation** happens inside the female's body	**menstruation**	the monthly loss of the **uterus** lining from a woman's body through the **vagina**
invertebrate	an animal without a backbone		
irritant	may cause reddening or blistering of the skin (Hazard label)	**microscope**	used to examine very small living **organisms**
joules	units of energy	**migration**	the movement of animals across long distance in search of food
kingdom	living things can be divided into five kingdoms e.g. the animal kingdom and the plant kingdom	**mineral oil**	crude oil usually found deep below ground, formed from the bodies of tiny sea creatures
labour	the time leading up to **birth** when the **uterus** muscles are contracting	**mixture**	two or more substances that are mixed together
lenses	the part of the **microscope** which makes a specimen look bigger	**model**	a way of imagining how something works
lichen	kind of plant	**moon**	large, usually rocky, object orbiting a planet
light year	a measure of distance – distance light travels in one year.	**mote**	a small **particle** of dust
lime	everyday name for calcium oxide	**moult**	when animals lose their thick fur during the summer
limewater	another name for calcium hydroxide solution	**move**	when a living thing, or part of a living thing, goes from one place to another
living organism	something showing all of life's characteristics		
lubrication	putting a substance between two surfaces to reduce friction	**naked eye**	looking at objects without a telescope or binoculars
luminous	describes an object that creates its own light (Sun)	**nerve cell**	carries messages around the human body
lunar eclipse	when the Moon moves through the Earth's shadow	**neutral**	neither **acid** nor **alkali**
lux	the units in which light **intensity** is measured	**neutralisation**	using up or cancelling out an **acid** or **alkali** to make it **neutral**
magnetic attraction	north and south poles pulling towards each other	**neutralised**	made **neutral**
		newtons	unit of force
magnification	how much bigger an image is than the object	**nocturnal**	an animal which is active at night and sleeps during the day
mammary glands	these make milk for a young baby	**non-renewable energy resource**	energy resource that once used is not replaced
mass	how much material you have		

non-luminous	describes an object that does not give out its own light, can be seen by reflecting light (Moon)
noon	time of day when the Sun is at its highest
North Pole	point at the northern end of the Earth's axis
Northern Hemisphere	half of the Earth north of the equator
nucleus	controls what happens inside a **cell**
nutrition	the process of making, getting and using food
omnivore	an animal which eats both plants and other animals
orbit	movement of one body around another (Earth around Sun, Moon around Earth)
organ	a structure in a plant or animal which has a special function and is made up of **tissues**
organism	a living thing
ovaries	make egg cells in humans and plants
oviduct	the tube connecting the **ovaries** with the **uterus**
ovulation	the release of an egg cell from the **ovaries** into the **oviduct**
oxide	substance containing **oxygen** joined to something else
oxygen	colourless gas that rekindles a glowing splint
palisade tissue	the **tissue** inside a leaf which makes food
parallel circuit	circuit with more than one route for current flow
particles	tiny bits of something
penis	places **sperm** inside a female's **vagina** during **sexual intercourse**
period	see **menstruation**
pH paper	**Universal Indicator** on filter paper to make it easy to use
pH scale	range of strength of **acids** and **alkalis**, from 1 to 14
pH values	numbers that mean how **acid** or **alkaline** something is
phases of the Moon	the different shapes of the Moon that we see
philosopher	a thinker, who tries to work out what's going on and why
placenta	the **organ** through which the developing baby gets food and oxgyen and gets rid of waste during **pregnancy**
planets	large spheres orbiting the Sun
polarity	when a device has a positive and a negative end
poles	positive and negative ends of a **cell**
pollen cell	the male **gamete** in plant **cells**
pollination	the transfer of a pollen grain from the **anther** of one plant to the **stigma** of another
predator	an animal which hunts other animals for food
pregnant	a mother is **pregnant** when a baby is growing and developing inside her
premature	when a baby is born early, before it is fully grown and developed
pre-menstrual tension	the tense feeling women sometimes have immediately before their monthly period
pressure	the force that a gas pushes with
prey	an animal which is hunted and eaten by another animal
primary consumer	the first animal in a **food chain**; it always eats the **producer**
producer	plants which make their own food using energy from the sun
product	a substance that is made during a **chemical change**
properties	the characteristics of a substance

protein	useful chemical found in some foods	**solar energy**	energy from the Sun
puberty	the time during **adolescence** when **secondary sexual characteristics** develop	**solar panel**	device to collect **solar energy** as heat
		solubility	how much **solute** dissolves in a **solvent**
reactant	a substance that reacts with something during a **chemical change**	**soluble**	a substance that will dissolve in a **solvent**
red blood cell	carries oxygen around the body	**solute**	a substance that has dissolved in a **solvent**
renewable energy resource	**energy resource** that is continually replaced	**solution**	mixture of a **solvent** and one or more **solutes**
reproduce	make new living things	**solvent**	a liquid that will dissolve something
reproductive organs	the **organs** used to make a new living thing	**South Pole**	point at the southern end of the Earth's **axis**
resistance	a measure of how difficult it is for electric **current** to flow	**Southern Hemisphere**	half of the Earth south of the **equator**
ring main	electrical **circuit** used in houses for lighting and power	**specialised**	see **adapted**
rock salt	the mixture of salt and rock that is found underground	**species**	living things which have almost all of their features in common
root hair cell	absorbs water from the soil	**specimen**	the name for anything you look at using a **microscope**
sandstone	a kind of rock	**sperm cell**	the male **gamete** in humans
saturated solution	a solution that can't dissolve any more solute	**stain**	the liquid you can add to a **specimen** to make it easier to see using a **microscope**
secondary consumer	the second animal in a **food chain**; it always eats the **primary consumer**	**stamen**	the part of a flower which makes pollen in its **anthers**
secondary sexual characteristics	the physical features you develop during **puberty**	**stigma**	the part of a flower where pollen grains must land for **pollination** to happen
series circuit	electrical **circuit** with only one possible route around it	**still**	a device for **distilling** a mixture
sex cell	another word for **gamete**	**stomach**	the organ which processes your food
sexual intercourse	when a man puts **sperm** into a woman's **vagina** using his **penis**	**streamlined**	a thin and pointed shape which moves easily through water
short circuit	a route around a component in a **circuit**, with very little **resistance**	**switch**	device to disconnect or connect **components** in a **circuit**
slide	the piece of glass upon which you place your **microscope specimen**	**symbol**	sign that means something
		taxonomy	another word for **classifying**
solar cell	device to transform sunlight directly into electricity	**temperature**	how hot or cold something is

testes	the place where **sperm** are made in humans
theory	idea
thermometer	device for measuring **temperature**
time zones	regions of the Earth which have a common time
tissue	a group of similar **cells** which work together to do the same job
transfer of energy	moving energy from one place to another
transforming energy	changing energy from one type to another
umbilical cord	this connects the **fetus** to the **placenta** inside the **uterus**
Universal Indicator	mixture of dyes that show the strength of an **acid** or **alkali**
upthrust	force of water or other liquid/gas pushing an object upwards
urine	liquid waste from animals
uterus	the organ in which a baby develops inside its mother
vacuole	contains the **cell** sap (a store of water, salt and sugar)
vagina	the place inside the woman where **sperm** are placed during **sexual intercourse**
variation	the way in which living things look different from each other
vertebrate	an animal with a backbone
virus	an organism which causes disease by living inside other living things
volts	unit of electrical push
volume	a space
waters breaking	when the **amniotic fluid** passes out of the mother before **birth**
weight	the force of **gravity** on a **mass**
zygote	the **cell** which is made after **fertilisation**

Index